The Pomerance Collection
of Ancient Art

The Pomerance Collection
of Ancient Art

THE BROOKLYN MUSEUM

The Pomerance Collection consists of ancient art objects owned by Mr. & Mrs. Leon Pomerance, Bernard Pomerance, Michael Pomerance, individually and jointly, and several pieces owned by the L. & H. Pomerance Foundation.

Catalogue of an exhibition held at

THE BROOKLYN MUSEUM

June 14 to October 2, 1966

Designed by Bernard Wolff

Lithographed by S. D. Scott Printing Co.

Contents

Abbreviations   8

Preface   9

Foreword   10

Ancient Near Eastern Art   13

Ancient Egyptian Art   59

Ancient Greek Art   67

Etruscan Art   103

Kato Zakro   124

Bibliography   126

Abbreviations Used in the Text

AAAO	H. Frankfort, *The Art and Architecture of the Ancient Orient* (Baltimore, 1955)
AAAO²	H. Frankfort, *The Art and Architecture of the Ancient Orient* (2nd edition, Baltimore, 1959)
AJA	*American Journal of Archaeology*
Ancient Art	New York, Metropolitan Museum of Art, *Ancient Art from New York Private Collections; Catalogue of an Exhibition Held at the Metropolitan Museum of Art, December 17, 1959-February 28, 1960,* by D. von Bothmer (New York, 1961)
BASOR	*Bulletin of the American Schools of Oriental Research*
BMFA	*Bulletin of the Museum of Fine Arts* [Boston]
BMMA	*Bulletin of the Metropolitan Museum of Art* [New York]
CANES	Committee of Ancient Near Eastern Seals, *Corpus of Ancient Near Eastern Seals in North American Collections, I. The Collection of the Pierpont Morgan Library,* catalogued and edited by E. Porada with B. Buchanan (New York, 1948), 2 v. (text and plates)
Cesnola, *Atlas*	L. P. di Cesnola, *A Descriptive Atlas of the Cesnola Collection of Cypriote Antiquities in the Metropolitan Museum of Art* (Boston, 1884-1903), 3 v.
CS	H. Frankfort, *Cylinder Seals; A Documentary Essay on the Art and Religion of the Ancient Near East* (London, 1939)
CVA	*Corpus Vasorum Antiquorum. . .* (Paris and elsewhere, 1922 ff.)
Glass from the Ancient World	R. W. Smith, *Glass from the Ancient World: The Ray Winfield Smith Collection; [Catalogue of] a Special Exhibition* (Corning, N. Y., 1957)
ILN	*The Illustrated London News*
Queens College Catalogue	Queens College, Flushing, N. Y., *Man in the Ancient World; An Exhibition of Pre-Christian Objects from the Regions of the Near East, Egypt, and the Mediterranean, February 10-March 7, 1958* (Flushing, N. Y., 1958)
Sale Catalogue	[Refers to a catalogue of a collection or objects sold at auction.]
"Sumptuary Arts. . ."	E. L. B. Terrace, "Sumptuary Arts of Ancient Persia," *Bulletin of the Museum of Fine Arts* [Boston] 63 (1965), pp. 3-31
University of Pennsylvania Catalogue	The University Museum, University of Pennsylvania, *What We Don't Know, An Exhibit from Private Collections in Honor of The Fourth International Congress of Classical Studies, August 24-29, 1964* (Philadelphia, 1964)

Preface

In the preparation of the present exhibition we have followed the wish of the Pomerance family to include with their objects complimentary materials, such as maps, books, and photographs, in order to indicate the wide range of culture the collection so admirably reflects.

Since the pieces shown are representative of the arts and cultures of the ancient world from Italy to Persia and cover a period of more than three thousand years, the entries in this catalogue have been arranged in broad geographical and chronological groupings. Further, an attempt has been made in each entry to provide some general background about the peoples who made the objects, and the times in which they lived. Each of the objects in the exhibition is illustrated in the catalogue. In selecting comparative material, the emphasis has been on pieces readily accessible in American institutions, particularly those in the New York and Boston areas.

The photographs shown in the exhibition together with the map and bibliography included in this catalogue will, it is hoped, contribute to the understanding of a fine collection and increase its appeal to the amateur of archaeology as well as to the specialist.

Many persons have contributed to this catalogue. Our first thanks are due to Harriet and Leon Pomerance, sensitive collectors who have made the objects and relevant information concerning them available; and have provided many of the photographs that appear on these pages. In addition to those whose names appear on the title page, to whom we are particularly indebted, we owe especial thanks to Dr. Dietrich von Bothmer who has provided valuable observations on the material of the last two sections as well as editorial suggestions. Mrs. Emeline Richardson has graciously commented on the several Etruscan bronzes. Mr. Andrew J. Oliver contributed information on the *askos*, No. 117 and other assistance. Dr. Kyle M. Phillips, Jr. has given biographical sources and date for the Etruscan mirror, No. 126. Mr. Andrew Ramage supports the attribution of the *lekythos*, No. 115. Much practical assistance has been rendered by the staffs of the Department of Ancient Art and the Wilbour Library of Egyptology of the Brooklyn Museum and by Miss Gale Sasson and Mrs. Rachel Varat.

JEAN L. KEITH

Foreword

It is sometimes assumed that the extraordinary growth of museums in the United States during the past few decades has hampered the formation of important personal collections of antiquities and other works of art, and that the interests of museum and private collector are, of necessity, opposed. Nothing could be further from the truth. The very size of the large museum, with its necessarily complicated organization, makes its system of purchasing somewhat elaborate, and this gives the private collector an advantage if he is knowledgeable, perceptive, and knows his own mind. He is able to act, as the museum cannot and should not, in a spontaneous way. The result of this will be apparent if the private collector does not merely seek that which has long been known and sought after, and if he does not acquire at vast expense works of art already enshrined, as it were, by réclame. If he seeks in less well ploughed fields, his collection may arouse more lively curiosity and give greater satisfaction. The objects contained in it will often reflect the active interest of the present day, no matter how great the actual age of those objects.

Mr. and Mrs. Leon Pomerance have, in the short space of twelve years, formed a remarkable collection and this they have done in no haphazard way. They have not been interested in merely assembling a number of *objets d'art* which have nothing in common but 'beauty,' though many of the pieces of which it is composed do have that elusive quality that is so hard to define. The collection was formed as the result of much devoted study and appreciation of the arts and the craftsmanship of ancient peoples. Many objects come from areas which are now the subject of archaeological investigation and discussion to ascertain what people lived in those regions, whence they came, what they made, and what they imported. Mr. and Mrs. Pomerance, exercising a spirit of adventurousness in acquiring pieces of this nature, kindle our present lively interest and encourage us in our search for further knowledge.

Mr. and Mrs. Pomerance's interest in archaeology played a great part in the formation of their collection but another aspect of that interest is called to mind in this exhibition by a cabinet of photographs of some objects found in the excavations of Minoan Kato Zakro in eastern Crete. They came mostly from the large cult depository found in 1963. The work in which the Pomerances became involved, is conducted under the expert supervision of Dr. Nikolas Platon for a short period each year. There is no doubt that this personal contact of the Pomerances with the unearthing of ancient artifacts, with the attendant problems always presented by newly found material, has fanned an enthusiasm already well manifested for the art of the islands and lands of the eastern half of the Mediterranean and extending into Iran.

The art of this area as represented in this exhibition is the product of many civilizations, various religions, and several empires. Some of the objects to be seen in this collection were made for palaces that were built for kings at Tell el Amarna, Nineveh, and Persepolis. Others were furnishings for simple people who lived in humble villages or tents. Great differences are therefore to be expected and these can easily be seen, but perhaps less obvious are the connecting links between much of this material. The work done on the wall of a king's palace may show details of the common soldiery and reveal that the Assyrian archers are barefoot whereas the warrior with his wicker shield is well shod. The art of one civilization affected that of others, the symbols and representations of mythical beings of one religion might be employed by another. Many of these were commonly found in the possessions of rich and poor, great and small, and were used in many countries for several centuries.

Much of this interplay of symbols, subjects and styles is reflected in the works of art in this collection. The resemblances and the diversities, within the boundaries set consciously and unconsciously by those who formed the collection, make it fascinating to us. Each piece has 'spoken' to its owners or it would not be here, and these one hundred and forty-two objects are not just that number of individual voices; they are an ensemble that has a character and intricate message of its own.

When the roles of a private collector and a museum are properly integrated, the result is fruitful and beneficial to both. Each supplements the other in an aim to interest and instruct. The catalogue, which so carefully describes in detail and illustrates each object in the Pomerance Collection exhibited here, is divided into sections: Ancient Near East, which includes material of types unknown until recent years; Egypt; Greece; and Etruria. This catalogue, which by its very nature deals with individual items, nonetheless draws us on to other works of art, and the exhibition, being held within the framework of a large museum, encourages us to blend the particular with the general. All conspires to let us achieve that synthesis necessary for the acquisition of knowledge. The display of the collection in The Brooklyn Museum galleries where there is space for added information rather than in the rooms of a comfortable house, while depriving the Pomerances temporarily of a great pleasure, enables them to fulfill their belief that a personal collection is not something only and always to be privately enjoyed, but rather something to be shared. Shared so that it may awaken in others the interest that has been their own, and arouse a desire to understand, as well as appreciate, the skills and arts of the human race.

Mr. and Mrs. Pomerance, by so generously lending their collection for exhibition within the hospitable walls of The Brooklyn Museum, give us all such an opportunity. It is here not as a means of escape from the present into the past but to help open our eyes to see what was then achieved, to enable us to perceive that, despite all the changes of form, style and meaning, such art can still speak to us and excite our present interest and, in so doing, be an inspiration for the future.

CHARLES K. WILKINSON

ANCIENT NEAR EASTERN ART

E.L.B. Terrace

1 Nude Worshiper

Sumerian
Probably Jemdet Nasr Period, toward 3000 B.C.
Gypsum
Height: 17 cm ($6^{11}/_{16}$ in.)

The corroded condition of the surface leaves the style of the sculpture somewhat equivocal. It is, however, probably to be attributed to the Jemdet Nasr Period. Although he is called here a worshiper there is no certainty that he is, only the likelihood that on such an object as this a sacred scene would have been represented. The man appears to be drawing a rope in both hands; perhaps he leads a temple herd.

The fragment is apparently the corner of a trough similar to a well-known example probably from Warka.

Cf. *AAAO*[2] pl. 3 C for the Warka trough, and pl. 6 A, C, for the double girdle on otherwise naked figures of the Jemdet Nasr Period. Figures in relief of this kind are best known from the "Warka Vase," E. Strommenger, *Fünf Jahrtausende Mesopotamien* (Munich, 1962), pls. 19-22.

2 Cattle in Landscape: impression of a cylinder seal

Sumerian
Uruk Period, about 3500-3200 B.C.
Green schist
Height: 2.6 cm (1.0 in.)   Diameter: 1.1 cm ($^{7}/_{16}$ in.)

This pastoral scene of a cow and its calf walking among plants is very like the well-known seal of the Uruk Period in the Louvre (A 26). It would appear that in our seal ears of grain are represented in a more cursory way than the much more explicit detail shown on Louvre seal A 26 and the fragment of another seal in the Louvre (A 116). On the other hand, the plant may represent one of the swamp grasses growing in the marshy edges of the river in southern Mesopotamia. The subject here, as in the others just cited, is obviously the fecundity of the herds.

Cf. *CS*, pl. V, 6: Louvre A 26, *Encyclopédie photographique de l'art*, II (Paris, 1936), p. 69, no. 21, Louvre A 116.

3 Worshiper with Hands Folded

Sumerian, said to be from Tello
Early Dynastic Period, shortly after 2500 B.C.
Gypsum
Height: 31 cm (12³⁄₁₆ in.)

A man with shaven head stands with hands folded together across his breast. He wears a sheepskin garment with four fringes. The position is the time-honored one of the humble and obeisant worshiper. Such statues were placed in the temples where they stood before the gods.

Although the bottom of the skirt is beginning to disengage itself from the block at the base against which the feet are carved, the treatment of the head and its details is still summary and approaches that of the period of Entemena.

Cf. for period of Entemena, G. Conteneau, *Manuel d'archéologie orientale*, II (Paris, 1931), pp. 548-549, and A. Parrot, *Tello* (Paris, 1948), pl. IV b. For a freer treatment in similar form, see *AAAO*, pl. 21.

4 Foundation Figure

Sumerian
Shortly after 2500 B.C.
Cast copper
Height: 20.6 cm (8⅛ in.)

The laying of a ceremonial cornerstone is not a new custom. Instead of depositing newspapers and other mementos of the age, the ancient Mesopotamians thought it vital to include statuettes of deities or rulers for the propitious future of the buildings they erected. Such a figure is this cast copper deity with his hands folded together. The horns surmounting his head tell us that a deity is represented. Although the long, tapering body suggests that these figures were originally pushed into the ground like pegs (and some have been found used this way), they are usually found in boxes together with other significant objects such as model bricks.

BIBLIOGRAPHY: *Ancient Art*, no. 20.
For foundation figures in general, see E. D. Van Buren, *Foundation Figurines and Offerings* (Berlin, 1931), and especially figs. 4-6 for this type (period of Entemena).

5 King Shulgi Carrying a Basket of Mortar

Neo-Sumerian
About 2100 B.C.
Cast copper
Height: 24.3 cm (9⁹⁄₁₆ in.)

In the Neo-Sumerian Period it was the custom to place
figures in the foundation deposits which carried the materials (bricks and mortar) used in the construction of the
temples. Although the figures are still tapered below the
waist as in the Sumerian Period, they are now invariably
found in boxes, their original function as cones or pegs
being remembered only in the shape. The Pomerance
foundation figure is so close in appearance to exactly
similar figures of the Neo-Sumerian king Shulgi excavated
at Nippur, that it is safe to assume that it, too, represents
this ruler of the Sumerian renaissance.

BIBLIOGRAPHY: Queens College Catalogue, no. 11.
Cf. *BMMA* 18 (1960), p. 250, fig. 9 (Shulgi from Nippur).

6 Stylized Animals: impression of a cylinder seal

Sumerian
Jemdet Nasr Period, toward 3000 B.C.
Dull black serpentine
Height: 5.3 cm (2 1/16 in.)   Diameter 2.2 cm (3/4 in.)

During the Jemdet Nasr Period, a breakdown of forms occurred in the style of seal engraving. This is first manifest in increased use of the drill, with interconnecting lines between drill holes in place of modeling. Ultimately, a completely linear style was developed in which all mass was jettisoned in favor of interweaving linear patterns, known as the "Brocade" style in the Early Dynastic I Period. This seal still retains a degree of form in the bodies of the animals which include a frog, a bird, and a goat (?).

Cf. for laddering of bird's wings *CS*, pl. VII k.

7 Animals and Other Patterns: impression of a cylinder seal

Sumerian
Jemdet Nasr Period, toward 3000 B.C.
Black serpentine
Height: 2.6 cm (1.0 in.)   Diameter: 2.5 cm (1.0 in.)

In addition to two horned and furry animals the decoration includes an "eye" pattern and a cursorily drawn fish, both found frequently on Jemdet Nasr seals.

Cf. for eye and fish *CS*, pl. VII b.

8 Birds: impression of a cylinder seal

Sumerian
Jemdet Nasr Period, toward 3000 B.C.
Mottled, dark grey serpentine
Height: 4.1 cm (1 5/8 in.)   Diameter: 1.7 cm (1 1/16 in.)

Two birds are shown: one standing in front view, the other striding in profile.

Cf. for the wings *CS*, pl. VII k.

9 Enthroned Figure Receiving Worshipers: impression of a cylinder seal

Old Babylonian
About 1800-1700 B.C.
Hematite or magnetite
Height: 2.7 cm (1 1/16 in.)   Diameter: 1.1 cm (7/16 in.)

A king or god, enthroned and holding a cup, receives a bald-headed worshiper wearing a long mantle. Behind him stands a goddess with arms upraised in supplication. Before the seated figure is a sun-disc in a crescent, but this does not necessarily identify the figure as a sun-god. At his knee is a human head in profile. Behind the worshiper's head are three globes which appear on other seals of the period, and whose significance is as yet unexplained. Before the goddess stands a lion-headed staff.

Behind stands the god with a crook who, in this case, carries another crook over his right(?) shoulder. One foot is raised on a small platform which may represent a mountain. Behind this deity is a squatting, ithyphallic dwarf, and below a curious linear representation which is apparently a lion. Typical of many Old Babylonian seals is the large number of smaller figures and symbols. Sometimes they may be readily identified, but more frequently whatever magical or sacred significance they once had, is now lost to us. On this score, the texts are rarely if ever helpful.

Cf. Old Babylonian seals, *CANES* I, pp. 39 ff.

10 Winged Hero Seizing Two Caprids: impression of a cylinder seal

Neo-Assyrian
Eighth to Seventh Century B.C.
Pale pinkish-grey chalcedony
Height: 3.1 cm (1 1/4 in.)   Diameter: 1.4 cm (9/16 in.)

The heraldic design of a hero with an animal on either side of him was already established in the Uruk Period, became the common pattern in Akkadian times, and was a standard theme of Neo-Assyrian seals. In this example, the hero has four wings; he is wearing the standard Assyrian robe and has one leg exposed. The style of carving is interesting because of its use of the drill as a purely stylistic mannerism. This custom had found favor in the Jemdet Nasr era and was used periodically thereafter, but it predominates in a specific class of Neo-Assyrian seals.

Cf. *CANES* I, pp. 83 ff.

11 Soldiers at War in a Mountainous District

Assyrian, from Nineveh
Reign of Sennacherib, 705-681 B.C.
Limestone
Length: 79.7 cm (31⅜ in.)

Of the many Assyrian reliefs in America, the great majority are large slabs from the palace of Assurnasirpal at Nimrud, most of them depicting heroic winged figures attending sacred trees. In 1959 a group of highly important historical reliefs from the palace of Sennacherib at Nineveh was sold at auction in London. These had lain hidden for many years in the house of Lady Charlotte Guest, a cousin of their excavator, Sir Henry Layard. Three of them came to America, two to the Museum of Fine Arts, Boston, the third to the Pomerance Collection. The latter fragment shows at the left an Assyrian soldier, in crested helmet and carrying a wicker(?) shield, who begins to climb the rocky hillside. On the right, two short-bearded, bushy-haired soldiers, the inhabitants of these mountains, fend off with bow and shield the attacking Assyrian cavalry, of which only the nose and foreleg of a horse are preserved. W. S. Smith discovered that this block joins one of those owned by the Boston Museum. The Boston block (MFA 60.134) preserves more of the file of Assyrian soldiers climbing the mountainside as well as another group of mountaineers being attacked by the cavalry. Note the added detail given to the hillside on which the soldiers are climbing.

BIBLIOGRAPHY: Sale Catalogue (London), *Sotheby* 16 November 1959, p. 14, no. 57 (ill.); *Ancient Art*, no. 34 and pl. 11; W. S. Smith, "Two Assyrian Reliefs from Canford Manor," *BMFA* 58 (1960), pp. 44 ff., especially fig. 5.

12 Fertility Figure

Syrian
Early Second Millennium B.C.
Terracotta
Height: 18.1 cm (7⅛ in.)

Of all the fertility and mother goddess figures of Western and Near Eastern art, these pottery figures from Syria are among the strangest. Although far removed from the obese sculptures of neolithic Europe and Asia and the heavy-hipped females of Marlik, they leave no doubt as to their purpose. Characteristic of the type represented here are the pierced top-knot and lug-like ears, the beak nose, heavy collar, prominent breasts and navel. Some of the figures clearly mean to expose the female genitals, but this one and others like it are not so certain and we cannot tell if the roughly picked girdle protects the private parts or circles the hips above them. In some cases tattooing may be represented as on certain Egyptian so-called concubine figures.

Cf. H. Th. Bossert, *Altsyrien* (Tübingen, 1951), nos. 628-630.

13 Stylized Idol

Syrian
Second Millennium B.C.
Steatite
Height: 7 cm (2¾ in.)

This figure, apparently a female fertility figure like No. 12, represents the ultimate development of a line of stylization of which No. 12 is an earlier phase. Here the top-knot has become the upper face with gigantic eyes, the nose a kind of weird afterthought, the arms crossed in front mere vestiges. The navel is greatly enlarged and below it a row of holes no doubt represents the girdle. By comparison with these distortions, the transition from abdomen to thighs is almost naturalistic.

BIBLIOGRAPHY: The Israel Museum, *The Bible in Archaeology*, [Exhibition] Catalogue no. 6 (Jerusalem, 1965), p. 52, no. 36.

14 Goddess with a Long Skirt

Phoenician
About Seventeenth Century B.C.
Bronze
Height: 26.5 cm (10⅞₁₆ in.)

An enthroned goddess wears a long skirt decorated with knobs; she is also adorned with a necklace, and a tall knobbed crown. The group of Phoenician bronzes to which this interesting example belongs has been examined by D. P. Hansen, who sees them as belonging to the seventeenth century B.C., if not slightly later. All are characterized by somewhat uplifted heads, as if the upward-staring eyes signified more strongly the deities' presence. The most closely related example is the well-known "Louvre Goddess" which, like our bronze, is seated and wears a tall crown with enlarged top and button-like decoration around the headband. Again, like our bronze, her head is primitively plastic but the body is flat. Both arms are outstretched, the left hand clasped like ours, the other held up with palm outward as if in benediction.

BIBLIOGRAPHY: *Ancient Art*, no. 30, pls. 4, 10.
Cf. for the Louvre Goddess: Bossert, *Altsyrien*, nos. 581-582; Megiddo bronze: G. Loud, *Megiddo* II (Chicago, 1948), pl. 236, no. 24. For all references, see D. P. Hansen, "A Bronze in the Semitic Museum of Harvard University," *BASOR* 146 (1957), pp. 13 ff.; referred to by A. Parrot, *Le Musée du Louvre et la Bible* (Paris, 1955), p. 61, n. 1.

15 Bearded Figure

Syrian
Middle of the Second Millennium B.C.
Copper
Height: 38.5 cm (15³⁄₁₆ in.)

The group of similar figures to which this interesting example belongs has been fully discussed by H. Seyrig. The modern history of the Pomerance statuette dates at least from 1901; the object passed through several collections before coming into its present ownership. The date of the group has been discussed often, but Hansen's attribution to the Middle Bronze Period is no doubt correct. In fact, the modeled heads and relatively flat bodies of these figures relate them chronologically to such figures as No. 14, also of the Middle Bronze Period. On the other hand, there is obviously in the Lebanon Mountain group a distinct traditional connection with the Judeideh (North Syria) bronzes of the Early Bronze Period, about 2800 B.C.

Since some of these bronzes seem to carry weapons, they have sometimes been called warriors. In fact, it is much likelier that they represent warrior gods. Some of these figures (including the similar bronze now in the Schimmel Collection) were found together in an eroded ridge in the mountains of central Lebanon, which suggests the possibility that they had been deposited together as a votive offering in a "sacred cave" or shrine to the local deity of war.

BIBLIOGRAPHY: O. Weber, *Hethitische Kunst* (Berlin, 1922), pl. 30; Val. Müller, *Frühe Plastik in Griechenland und Vorderasien* (Augsburg, 1929), p. 107, no. 13; S. Ronzevalle in *Mélanges de l'Université St. Joseph* [Beirut], 19 (1935), pl. IX 1; F. W. von Bissing in *Mélanges . . . Dussaud* 2 (1939), p. 752, fig. 2 a; Bossert, *Altsyrien*, no. 607; M. Gjødesen in *Meddelelser fra Ny Carlsberg Glyptotek* 8 (1951), p. 25; H. Seyrig, "Statuettes trouvées dans les montagnes du Liban," *Syria* 30 (1953), pp. 24 ff. and p. 28, no. 7.
Cf. D. P. Hansen, "A Bronze in the Semitic Museum of Harvard University." *BASOR* 146 (1957), pp. 13 ff., especially p. 18, n. 25. For the Schimmel bronze, see H. Hoffmann, ed., *Norbert Schimmel Collection* (Cambridge, Mass., 1964), no. 60 (date given therein too early), correct reference given there to *Syria* 30 (1953), pl. 11, fig. 2.

16   Enthroned God with Gold Crown

Phoenician
About Fourteenth Century B.C.
Bronze, with gold foil on crown and upper part of body
Height: 14.8 cm (5¹³⁄₁₆ in.)

This bronze falls into the group of figures which are slightly more modeled than such examples as No. 14, and for that reason may be dated about the fourteenth century B.C. A somewhat similar object, although much flatter, is a gold-foil-covered bronze from Megiddo, excavated in a Late Bronze Period context, with a date ranging from the fourteenth to the twelfth century B.C. Often the personage represented in this form is referred to as Baal, although there is no inscriptional evidence for this association. The original seat or throne is missing.

BIBLIOGRAPHY: Queens College Catalogue, pp. 14 and 30, no. 16 (ill.). Cf. Loud, op. cit., pls. 237-238, no. 30. See Hansen, op. cit.

17   Warrior God

Syrian
Late Second Millennium B.C.
Bronze
Height: 24.9 cm (9¹³⁄₁₆ in.)

The god wears the Egyptianizing crown with bulbous top, a knee-length kilt the waist and hem of which are rolled, and he carries a short stick or lance which may be broken off above the closed fist. The eyes are represented by a depression across the face, passing directly through the bridge of the nose.

For the treatment of eyes and nose cf. Bossert, Altsyrien, no. 595.

18   Group of Four Personnages

Syrian
Early First Millennium B.C.
Bronze
Height: 22.1 cm ($8^{11}/_{16}$ in.)

The identity of these four figures is a mystery, but it is likely that they are a group of deities. The one on the right carries what is probably a weapon, and all are presumably male. These curiously flat and highly stylized figures joined together in mutual embraces belong to a class which seems to have been made in Syria in the early first millennium B.C.

BIBLIOGRAPHY: *Ancient Art*, no. 29 and pl. 4.
Cf. Bossert, *Altsyrien* Nos. 599-600 (599 = Conteneau in *Syria* 8 [1927] pl. XLVIII, Louvre AO 2772).

19   Head of a Young Princess

Syrian
Fourteenth to Thirteenth Century B.C. (?)
Ivory
Height: 9.7 cm ($3^7/_8$ in.)

The object is the head of a youthful woman, wearing a wig of a type known in Egypt during the late XVIIIth Dynasty. The wig was made separately from the head, and was apparently stained with black. In the center over the forehead is a circular depression which probably took an attached uræus. A tendon in the neck was used to attach the head either to a statue or a piece of furniture.

Despite the explicitly Egyptian form of the wig, the head cannot be of Egyptian origin. The form of the face, with its typically depressed Syrian appearance in profile, and the type of mouth, unknown in Egypt during the late XVIIIth Dynasty when this kind of valanced wig was used, are enough to disprove Egyptian workmanship. In fact, this unparalleled sculpture might well have been made as a gift for a Syrian ruler to present to a pharaoh, possibly on the occasion of the marriage of a Syrian princess to the pharaoh or an Egyptian prince. This would explain the order in a Syrian court that a head be carved from precious ivory in the Egyptian taste, to be sent to the "royal brother" in Egypt, no doubt as part of the dowry.

Cf. for the Egyptian form of the wig, C. Aldred, "Hair Styles and History," *BMMA* 15 (1957) 141 ff. Internationalism in ancient art has been studied recently in W. S. Smith, *Interconnections in the Ancient Near East* (New Haven, 1965). Charles Wilkinson, with whom I discussed this highly interesting object, recalls to my attention a second millennium Syrian wooden statuette of a lady found in Upper Egypt, *BMMA* 18 (1960) 256, fig. 15.

20   Cow with Suckling Calf

North Syrian (Arslan Tash)
Ninth Century B.C.
Ivory plaque
Height: 5.7 cm (2¼ in.)   Width: 10.3 cm (4¹⁄₁₆ in.)

The subject is a common one on the ivories from Syria
and Assyria (the latter being, in most cases, of Syrian and
Phoenician manufacture). Like the "Goddess at the Window," the subject makes reference to the continuation of
fertility, which was so significant to the ancient mind.
Despite the hieratic nature of the subject, it is rendered
with an easy naturalism; note, for instance, how the
forward horn overlaps the one behind it. The manner in
which this subject is rendered is taken from direct ob-
servation of nature; who has not seen a cow turn her head
to lick her suckling calf? On the other hand, the plant
which frames the left edge is highly stylized.

Cf. S. Thureau-Dangin, *Arslan Tash* (Paris, 1931), pp. 135 ff., pls.
41-42.

21   Goddess at the Window

North Syrian (Arslan Tash)
Ninth Century B.C.
Ivory plaque with glass inlay
Height: 4.6 cm (1¹³⁄₁₆ in.)

Traditionally called the "Woman at the Window," the
subject is by no means easy to identify. Barnett identifies
her as a goddess, a Phoenician form of Aphrodite, who
represented the sacred sacrifice of virginity as it was
practiced in Phoenicia and Babylon. He has also identified the rectangular plaque on the front of her wig as an
apotropaic amulet. The elements at the bottom of the
object, which resemble tassels, are actually the bases of
columns surmounted directly by capitals. Remains of glass
inlay are preserved below the head of the goddess.

BIBLIOGRAPHY: Queens College Catalogue, pp. 14 and 31, no. 17 (ill.).
Cf. S. Thureau-Dangin, *op. cit.*, pls. 34-36. For the subject: R. D.
Barnett, *The Nimrud Ivories* (London, 1957), pp. 145 ff.

22 Comic Head

Said to have been found in Greece
Possibly Fourth Century B.C.
Polychrome glass
Height: 5.5 cm (2³⁄₁₆ in.)

The face and ears are opaque yellow glass, the details of brows, eyes and upper part of the beard are opaque dark blue. The locks over the forehead, moustache and beard are transparent greenish glass. The mouth and whites of the eyes are opaque white glass. This is a particularly finely made and handsome example of a type of glass figure made especially in the Eastern Mediterranean and Egypt at the end of the first millennium B.C. They were strung as beads, sometimes whole necklaces being made of smaller examples.

Cf. *Glass from the Ancient World*, pp. 96-97, no. 166.

23 Comic Head

Eastern Mediterranean
First Century B.C. to First Century A.D.
Polychrome glass
Height: 2.9 cm (1⅛ in.)

Like No. 22, this head has a suspension loop. The colors include white (face and ears), dark blue (hair, brows, eyeballs, rims of eyes, beard), yellow (earrings).

Again like No. 22, the hair is represented by coils of glass, but here the beard is massive. The earrings are an added touch.

24 Polychrome Oinochoe

Said to have been found in Greece
Fifth to Fourth Century B.C.
Glass
Height: 8.7 cm (3½ in.)

During the Hellenistic period, Greek shapes spread throughout the Mediterranean, and it is no surprise to find such typically Greek shapes as the handled oinochoe being used by the Eastern Mediterranean glassmakers. On the other hand, it is not impossible that those glass vessels which are found in Greece were made there. The trailing and marvering of glass threads of various colors in a matrix of solid color had been employed already in Egypt in the XVIIIth Dynasty, but the technique became a favorite of the Hellenistic manufacturers. In a dark blue matrix the following colors are trailed: light blue, yellow, black.

Cf. *Glass from the Ancient World*, pp. 28-29, no. 21. A particularly fine oinochoe of this period recently entered the Museum of Fine Arts, Boston (MFA 65.1748).

25 Tending of Animals: impression of a cylinder seal

Cappadocian
End of the Third Millennium B.C.
Pinkish chalcedony(?)
Height: 3.9 cm (1⁹⁄₁₆ in.)   Diameter: 2.7 cm (1¹⁄₁₆ in.)

In the upper register, a herd of goats or sheep is followed by a man carrying a bucket on a yoke. The pen in which the herd is kept is at the right. In the lower register men are engaged in several activities. At the left one figure extends an ear of grain(?) toward a seated figure who holds a plow(?). A gateway separates this group from another seated man who holds a handled pot. The interesting group on the right shows what may be a shearing or milking scene.

Cf. for Cappadocian seals *CS*, pp. 242 ff.

26 Four-wheeled Wagon Drawn by Two Bulls

Anatolian
Middle of the Second Millennium B.C. (?)
Bronze
Length: 23.5 cm (9¼ in.)

Not long ago a great many bronze carts drawn by oxen were discovered in Southern Anatolia. They have been dispersed gradually through the antiquities market. They range in size from small examples to quite large ones, while this cart is roughly middle-sized. Some are two-wheeled and others four-wheeled. Unfortunately, the circumstances of the discovery are unknown and it is impossible, from the evidence available, to date this find precisely. The general opinion is that they belong to the middle of the second millennium. Another wagon with four wheels and drawn by two bulls is now in the Museum of Fine Arts, Boston, and was acquired before the discovery of this new hoard. The Boston wagon is copper and more archaic in appearance than the Pomerance piece. In publishing it, I associated it with the pre-Hittite culture of Alaça Hüyük (about 2100 B.C.). Two warriors brandishing short swords—in all probability originally attached to the Boston wagon—may, however, indicate a later date. The whole question of these carts needs to be thoroughly studied.

Cf. Boston wagon: Terrace, "Recent Acquisitions in the Department of Egyptian Art," *BMFA* 62 (1964), pp. 56 ff. and fig. 12. A similar cart has recently been acquired by the Metropolitan Museum (66.15).

The Luristan Bronzes

The imagination of the art world was captured in 1928–1930 when there suddenly appeared in the antiquities market of Europe curious bronzes of a type hitherto unknown. Soon it was learned that they were being unearthed by the nomadic mountaineers of Luristan in Western Persia, and before long, hundreds, even thousands, of the bronzes came into the market. Only two controlled excavations have been undertaken in the region; see E. F. Schmidt, "The Second Holmes Expedition to Luristan," *Bulletin of the American Institute for Iranian Art and Archaeology* 5 (1938), pp. 205 ff.; and J. Meldgaard *et al.*, "Excavations at Tepe Guran, Luristan," *Acta Archaeologica* 34 (1963), pp. 97 ff.

The date (or dates, since there are recognizably separate chronological groupings) and cultural affinities of the bronzes have long been the subject of discussion. For some years it has been recognized that they may range in date from as early as about 1200 B.C. in some cases to as late as the sixth century B.C. in others. These dates have been more or less confirmed by Edith Porada in a recently published study which provides a more precise framework within which to make a more definitive attribution of different classes of the bronzes.

Basically, as has long been seen, the bronzes may be divided into two major groups, each of which is characterized by a specific technique of manufacture: (a) heavy cast objects; (b) much lighter hammered and chased objects. The cast objects, with which we are concerned here, may be subdivided into several types, the most common of which are horse gear and so-called standards or talismans. The heaviness and sometimes very elaborate decoration of the horse trappings suggest that they were not articles of utilitarian use, but rather formed part of funerary regalia. In fact, the implication is that the manufacturers of the bronzes had already left behind their nomadic ways and were now settled in a more sedentary life which permitted the setting up of an extensive bronze industry.

The so-called standards are heraldic groups of animals holding rings through which a central pin may be passed, and later on heraldic groups on either side of a central tube now decorated with combinations of human and animal heads. A primary feature of these standards is the use in the more complex (and presumably later) examples of what is called zoomorphic juncture, that is, the joining together of integral parts of one animal or human figure with those of another. A particularly explicit example is No. 29, in which the forelegs of the felines become the torso of the human figure, and the haunches and rear legs the lower part of the human figure. In the development of the bronzes the use of zoomorphic juncture becomes highly inventive. Edith Porada suggests that these heraldic groupings may derive from the ancient iconographic usage of animals on either side of a "sacred tree." In this case, the round and flat-topped pins found holding the bronzes together may be symbolical vestiges of the original plant ornament. Whether those standards whose centers are made up of human heads or figures (see No. 29 especially) are meant to represent the "master of the hunt" or the "master of the animals," we cannot say, but the possibility of such an association exists.

For references, see E. Porada, "Nomads and Luristan Bronzes; Methods Proposed for a Classification of the Bronzes," Chapter III in *Dark Ages and Nomads, ca. 1000 B.C.* (Istanbul, 1964), pp. 21-44 (where earlier bibliography is cited).

27 Bronze Standard

Luristan
About 800 B.C.
Height: 17.0 cm ($6^{11}/_{16}$ in.)

Two heraldic winged ibexes are drawn in a beautifully simplified outline style. The outline is made more vibrant by dentellation, which must be related to what has been called the serrated-wing style of certain Iranian cylinder seals of about the same time.

For references, see p. 30.

28 Bronze Standard

Luristan
About 900-800 B.C.
Height: 12.5 cm ($4^{15}/_{16}$ in.)

Two roaring felines hold rings through which a conical-topped pin is passed. The still somewhat naturalistic treatment of the haunches suggests that this standard may be slightly earlier than No. 27.

For references, see p. 30.

30 Bronze Standard

Luristan
About 800 B.C.
Height: 28 cm (11$\frac{1}{16}$ in.)

A highly ornamented standard is made up of various
fused figures and beasts. It stands on a vessel-shaped support which forms the basis for many of the standards.
This is an example of the most developed form of the
standards.

For references, see p. 30.

29 Bronze Standard

Luristan
About 800 B.C.
Height: 11.1 cm (4$\frac{3}{8}$ in.)

Two closely confronted felines rear their long necks upward to touch the head of a human figure. The head itself
has become a ring through which to pass a pin.

For references, see p. 30.

31 Bronze Standard

Luristan
About 800 B.C.
Height: 11.1 cm (4⅜ in.)

This is another decorative standard with stylized felines forming the body of a human figure.

For references, see p. 30.

32 Bronze Whetstone Handle

Luristan
About 900–800 B.C.
Height: 9.8 cm (3⅞ in.)

A well-known type of Luristan bronze is the whetstone handle which is frequently in the form of the forepart of an ibex. In this example the forms are still sufficiently naturalistic to place it somewhat earlier than the preceding bronze, No. 31.

For references, see p. 30.

33 Bronze Rein Ring

Luristan
About 800 B.C.
Height: 9.3 cm (3¹¹⁄₁₆ in.)

This rein ring is ornamented with animals and heroic heads. The horns of an ibex head join with horned heroic heads attacked by felines.

For references, see p. 30.

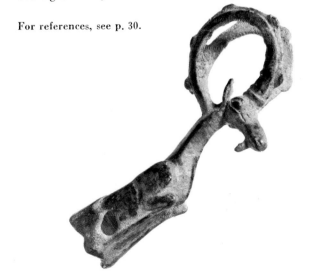

34   Bronze Cheek Plaque

Luristan
About Eighth to Seventh Century B.C.
Height: 8.9 cm (3½ in.)   Length: 11.2 cm (4⁷⁄₁₆ in.)

The plaque shows a roaring lion hitched to a wheeled
platform on which a kilted archer kneels. He holds a rein
which passes through a yoke. The casting was imperfect,
and the details of the upraised hand pulling back the
bowspring have become confused with what is apparently
a quiver hanging on the archer's back. The free treatment
of this plaque brings us to a later period in the series of
Luristan bronzes. Porada (*op. cit.*, pp. 27-28) suggests that
the unframed cheek plaques with animals modeled in
broad planes may be precursors of Achaemenian style and
should be dated to the late seventh and early sixth centuries B.C. If this is so, the present plaque must be slightly
earlier, because the treatment of the lion especially is
reminiscent of the "coiled" modeling found on such
bronzes as No. 35. On the other hand, the curly lock falling down the back of the archer's head reminds one of
the hammered and chased bronzes which are generally
later than the majority of the cast bronzes.

Apparently, this is the left side of a bit of which the
right side is in the Louvre. The slight differences may be
attributed to the separate casting of the two pieces.

Cf. for the Louvre check piece: R. Ghirshman, *Art of Ancient Iran*
(New York, 1964), fig. 73. The curly lock: *ibid.*, fig. 93. For references, see p. 30.

35   Bronze Figure

Luristan
About 800 B.C.
Height: 9.0 cm (3⁹⁄₁₆ in.)

This highly original figure is a fusion of several elements.
Basically it seems to be a female holding a baby to her
breast. The lower part of her body is rendered as an open-
work basket-like structure on which are attached rudimentary stick-like legs. But the most remarkable decorations are the various elements that are hung on rings
attached to the shoulders. These include a spoked ring, a
plain ring, a double-linked chain, and an ewer. What the
paraphernalia may represent is a complete mystery. The
coil-like modeling, derived from the wax model from
which it was cast and related to such modeling as that
found on No. 29, assures the Luristan origin of the piece.

Cf. *Ancient Art in American Private Collections* (Cambridge, Mass,
1954), p. 29, no. 186, pl. LVII, where an almost identical figure, but
without the dangling objects, is miscalled Greek "Geometric Period."

36 Bronze Figure

Payravand (?), Kurdistan
Early First Millennium B.C.
Height: 7.0 cm (2¾ in.)

The consistency of this class of figures is such as to indicate that they have a single provenance and similar date, which has not been entirely established. We do not know if they are apotropaic or prophylactic. The horned hero who protects the flocks and herds had existed so long in neighboring Mesopotamia that it is probable that these curious figures are really derived ultimately from their more sophisticated neighbors. They are always highly stylized, indeed organically rudimentary. Sometimes they are ithyphallic, like this example. Possible relationships between these figures, the horned mask No. 46, and certain terracotta figures from the South West Caspian have been touched on briefly in "Sumptuary Arts of Ancient Persia" (see Bibliography, p. 126).

For the Payravand figures, see L. Vanden Berghe, *L'Archéologie de l'Iran ancien* (Leiden, 1959), p. 111, pl. 138 b and c.

37 Bronze Figure

Payravand (?), Kurdistan
Early First Millennium B.C.
Height: 11.1 cm (4⅜ in.)

The figure is basically like No. 36, with slight differences noted elsewhere.

Bronzes of the South West Caspian: The Marlik Culture

In *7000 Years of Iranian Art* (Washington, 1964), pp. 16 ff., Edith Porada proposed the term "Marlik Culture" for the homogeneous culture group in the area of Iran southwest of the Caspian Sea. This area was formerly referred to as "Amlash," "North West Iran," "Dailaman," "South West Caspian," etc. The new term, on the analogy of Assyriological usage in Mesopotamia, is far more satisfactory. Bronzes and terracottas coming from the Amlash entrepôt have a consistency of features which relates them to the objects discovered in officially-controlled excavations at Marlik. Fortunately, the richness of these Marlik excavations has yielded varieties of materials which can in turn be related to more precisely dated materials elsewhere. Thus we can now say that the Marlik Culture began at least as early as 1200 B.C. and lasted for several centuries, although the precise stylistic and chronological development has yet to be established firmly. We are able to put together related groups of objects, and one of these is the class of bronze animals which is represented typically by the now familiar stiff-legged stags and humped Zebu bulls. As in the case of the Luristan bronzes, no texts provide information about the fertility cults or rites for which these little animals must have been made. That they had something to do with such rites is certain because of their association with steatopygous "mother-goddess" figures (see No. 44) made of bronze and terracotta. It is interesting to note that the prominence of the stag and bull suggests the two most important strains in this culture: the hunting, foraging nature of the nomad, and the settled, herd-raising life of a more sedentary people. In fact, the coincidence of the two types of bronze seems to bring us to the point of equilibrium between the two worlds of these people. Other animals belong to this lively creation: rams, ibexes, gazelles, horses, equestrian figures, dogs, etc. Besides the important stylistic contrast between the Marlik bronzes and the Luristan bronzes, there is another significant point of departure between them which is really responsible for the stylistic differences: this is the rejection of a fantastic, mythical imagery in Marlik and the representation of animals for their own sake in what might be called a basically naturalistic style.

For bibliography of Marlik and Marlik Culture, see Porada, *op. cit.*, p. 47; E. O. Negahban, "A Brief Report on the Excavation of Marlik Tepe and Pileh Qal'eh," *Iran* 2 (1964), pp. 13 ff.

38 Bronze Ram

Marlik Culture
About 1000 B.C.
Height: 2.6 cm (1 in.)

The ram has naturalistically curled horns. Note the transverse hole for stringing.

39 Bronze Stag

Marlik Culture
About 1000 B.C.
Height: 3.9 cm (1⁹⁄₁₆ in.)

40 Bronze Zebu Bull

Marlik Culture
About 1000 B.C.
Height: 3.8 cm (1½ in.)

Note the transverse hole through the body, for stringing, which is found in many of these bronzes.

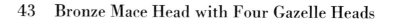

41   Bronze Pin with Bull Finial

Marlik Culture
About 1000 B.C.
Length: 27.8 cm (10^{15}/$_{16}$ in.)

This time, the bull forms the finial of a long pin which seems to extend the tail. A parallel (unpublished) is in the Heeramaneck Collection, New York.

42   Bronze Pin with Horse Finial

Marlik Culture
About 1000 B.C.
Height: 11.5 cm (4^{9}/$_{16}$ in.)

The horse, which is highly stylized, surmounts a pin with two square separators on the upper half. Their function is unexplained.

Cf. two similar horse-topped pins, Terrace, *The Art of the Ancient Near East in Boston* (Boston, 1962), no. 40, where they are incorrectly labelled "Luristan."

43   Bronze Mace Head with Four Gazelle Heads

Marlik Culture
About 1000 B.C.
Height: 6.5 cm (2^{9}/$_{16}$ in.)

This is an elegantly conceived object which, in its decoration, seems far removed from its stated purpose as an instrument of war. The gazelle heads are modeled in the finest style of Marlik. The form, with heads in the round, is reminiscent of the mace head with human heads from the Marlik excavations (almost identical to one in the Schimmel Collection). Similar gazelle heads are on a different type of mace head excavated at Marlik.

Cf. for the Schimmel and Marlik mace heads with human-head decorations, "Sumptuary Arts . . ." pp. 6-7, no. 2 (ill.). For the gazelle heads on a cylindrical mace head, see *ILN.* 5 May 1962, p. 701, fig. 17.

44 Steatopygous Lady

Marlik Culture
About 1000 B.C.
Buff Pottery
Height: 23 cm (9¹⁄₁₆ in.)

The heavy-hipped female figures from the Marlik Culture
are now known in a variety of forms, the common one
being represented by the example here. Characteristic of
all of them is the circular face with round eyes and beak-
like nose. Like other primitive and even not so primitive
cultures, the Marlik people obviously sought the symboli-
zation of fecundity in these exaggerated forms. Usually the
figures from Marlik are anthropoid vessels (although the
"spout" on this example is non-functional) which must
have been used as lustral vessels in some ceremony now
unknown to us.

Cf. *BMFA* 62 (1964), p. 61, fig. 19, for a large example (MFA
62.582); *Syria* 39 (1962), pp. 212-224 for other types.

45 Man with Earrings

Marlik Culture
Early First Millennium B.C.
Bronze
Height: 7.1 cm (2¹³⁄₁₆ in.)

This strange but delightfully humorous little man is
probably a citizen of the Marlik region. The straight legs
and hemispherical buttocks connect him with certain animals from that area. Earrings are found on Luristan and
Marlik bronzes, but these are especially elaborate examples. The chevron and hatched patterning on the torso
and legs is another unusual feature. Holes were drilled
through the triangular shoulders which were meant to
take separately attached arms, rings, or perhaps additional
coils. The genitals are somewhat exaggerated.

Cf. for the round buttocks *7000 Years of Iranian Art* (Washington,
1964), no. 49.

46 Mask of a Horned Deity

Iran
Early First Millennium B.C.
Bronze
Height: 22.1 cm (8¹¹⁄₁₆ in.)

The neck and face are highly stylized, but naturalistically sweeping horns emerge from the forehead. The ears are pierced, presumably to take earrings, four on each ear. The object is perhaps related to such figures as No. 44 and perhaps to the Payravand idols No. 36 and No. 37, but so far its exact provenance and precise cultural association are unknown. The Pomerance bronze represents a unique and important type. If its archaeological context is uncertain, at least we can say that as a work of art the mask has great authority and that it stands as another important monument to the individuality of the pre-Achaemenian metalworkers of Iran.

BIBLIOGRAPHY: Queens College Catalogue, pp. 15 and 34, no. 34 (ill.); *Ancient Art*, p. 11, no. 49, pls. 4 and 17; *Sept mille ans d' art en Iran* (Paris, 1961), p. 11, no. 27; *Le Figaro* (Paris), October 18, 1961, p. 1 (ill.); *Larousse Encyclopedia of Mythology* (New York, 1965), p. 190 (ill.); "Sumptuary Arts . . ." pp. 4 ff., no. 1 (ill.), with fuller discussion.

47 Head of a Lion-griffin

Northwest Iran
Early First Millennium B.C.
Bronze
Length: 19 cm (7½ in.)

The tall ears which are present on its companion in the Schimmel Collection are absent on this piece, but the holes for their attachment are located just above the ruff. Although almost identical, there are slight differences between the two objects. Most notable is the appearance on the Pomerance griffin of a scale or feather pattern delicately engraved on its neck. A tiny hole on the right side (missing on the other side, which is slightly restored) indicates that the griffin head was perhaps riveted to a chariot pole. The hole is too small for a handle, which would make this a drinking or pouring vessel.

The dramatic fierceness of these beasts reflects as its best the imaginative creativity of the early Iranian artist. In many ways they are naturalistic, yet the total form and its ornament are utterly decorative without repressing the vehement nature of the creatures. We have no idea to what mythological world this and other strange demons belong, but we may be sure that it was a frightening and awesome one filled with terror and uncertainty so great that all the artist's endeavors were devoted to the creation of what we must take for the representation of an apotropaic environment of new and powerful forces.

BIBLIOGRAPHY: *Ancient Art*, p. 9, no. 37, pls. 4, 12; *Sept mille ans d' art en Iran*, no. 286; *ILN* 2 April 1960, p. 551, fig. 5; Ghirshman in *Artibus Asiae* 25 (1962), pp. 57 ff., fig. 15; Wm. Culican, *The Medes and Persians* (New York, 1965), fig. 29; "Sumptuary Arts . . ." pp. 10 and 11, no. 6 (ill.), from which much of the above has been quoted. Cf. *Norbert Schimmel Collection*, no. 61, pp. 9 ff., no. 5.

48 Ibex about to Spring

Iran
Eighth to Seventh Century B.C.
Bronze, one iron horn preserved
Height 7.5 cm (2¹⁵⁄₁₆ in.)

The ibex has all four feet placed together on a molded cylinder which forms the top of a now-missing pin. Modeled in simple planes, but with much naturalism, the style is pre-Achaemenian, but not by many years. The bronze may reflect the naturalistic art of Assyria in the eighth to seventh century which spread to Iran and undoubtedly influenced the prevailing trends there. This led ultimately to the development of the Achaemenian style. The position of the ibex recalls the mouflon standing on the head of a woman (Foroughi Collection), an object which is perhaps Neo-Elamite in date. One is also reminded of caprids engraved on the bronze bands which decorated the Assyrian tub in which the Treasure of Ziwiyeh was discovered.

A charming conceit of our ibex is the multiple-floral earring.

Cf. for the mouflon in the Foroughi Collection: *7000 Years of Art in Iran*, pp. 72 and 139, no. 240 (ill.); Ziwiyeh bronze band: A. Godard, *Le Trésor de Ziwiyè* (Haarlem, 1950), fig. 9.

49 Caprids Kneeling before "Sacred Tree"

Ziwiyeh
Eighth to Seventh Century B.C.
Polychrome glazed earthenware
Height: 45.7 cm (18 in.)

Among the most interesting discoveries made at Ziwiyeh are the polychrome glazed vessels with representations of bulls and caprids kneeling before palmettes (the so-called sacred trees). There is much discussion about the origin of these vessels because of their great similarity to vessels of the same type and ware from the Neo-Assyrian levels of Assur, dated to the eighth to seventh century B.C. Edith Porada sees the Ziwiyeh vessels as of local manufacture because of certain, but very slight, divergences from the Assyrian examples we know. But within the relatively limited range of material from Assur there is already a variety of representational mannerisms which could easily account for the occasional peculiarities found at Ziwiyeh. Since the shapes of these Ziwiyeh vessels are precisely those of the Assur examples, and the ware the same, I prefer to see them as imports along with other Assyrian objects found at Ziwiyeh.

For the Ziwiyeh Treasure, see A. Godard, *op. cit.*, especially figs. 55-56; E. Porada, *The Art of Ancient Iran* (New York, 1965), p. 130, pl. 36 (vase in the Metropolitan Museum of Art). For the Assur vessels, see W. Andrae, *Coloured Ceramics from Ashur* (London, 1925), especially pl. 20.

50 Bulls Kneeling before "Sacred Tree"

Ziwiyeh
Eighth to Seventh Century B.C.
Polychrome glazed earthenware
Height: 47 cm (18½ in.)

The colors have disappeared, but traces of turquoise and white outlines may be observed. The "sacred tree" is really a palmette.

For references, see No. 49.

51 Glazed Earthenware Jar

Ziwiyeh
Eighth to Seventh Century B.C.
Height: 9.8 cm (3½ in.)

The fine turquoise color is nicely preserved on this vessel, which is also from the Ziwiyeh Treasure but presumably of Assyrian manufacture and imported into Ziwiyeh.

For similarly shaped and glazed vessels from Assur, see Andrae, *op. cit.*, figs. 18-19.

52 Heroes Conquering Lions: fragment from a quiver

Ziwiyeh
Late Seventh Century B.C.
Gold
Height: 14 cm (5½ in.)

The fragment of the quiver retains six frames, each containing identical scenes derived directly from Assyrian art: a robed and bearded figure slaying a lion with a sword. It becomes a highly popular subject in Persian art and in the Achaemenian period is found on reliefs and cylinder seals. The frames are separated by ridges and dots, and the two halves divided by a "guilloche." The outer edges are pierced with holes for attachment to whatever material the quiver was made of, possibly leather.

It is typical of Persian art that what had been elsewhere a subject inspired with heroism and sometimes even with pathos becomes more ornamental than dramatic. The drama is gone from these rigid figures, and we are left with a pattern pleasing to the eye, the original emotion of which we may come to intellectually but which is hardly significant instinctively. The hero slaying a lion may have a reference to an ancient Mesopotamian concept of the triumph of order (represented by the hero) over chaos (the lion symbolizing the forces of nature). That the artisans of Ziwiyeh were aware of Mesopotamian myth is shown by the curious scene on No. 53. On the other hand, the subject may simply refer to the prowess and bravery of the chieftain whose hunting equipment was once adorned with this plaque.

The frontispiece is a color plate of No. 52.

BIBLIOGRAPHY: *BMMA* 13 (1955), p. 220; University of Chicago, *Oriental Institute Annual Report 1958-59*, p. 17, fig. 8; "Sumptuary Arts . . ." pp. 14-15, from which some of the above has been quoted; P. Amandry and R. Ghirshman, *L'Or de la Perse* (in press).
Professor Helene Kantor believes this plaque comes from a quiver to which the following plaques also belong: Teheran, Archaeological Museum (Registers 6-8): Vanden Berghe, *op. cit.*, pl. 141 e; Louvre (Register 9): *Syria* 35 (1958), p. 182, fig. 7; Teheran, Archaeological Museum (Registers 11-12): Godard, *op. cit.*, p. 37, fig. 27; (Register 1): *Ancient Art*, p. 9, no. 39, pls. 12 and 102.

53 Epaulette with Mythical Scenes

Ziwiyeh
Late Seventh Century B.C.
Gold
Height: 22.5 cm (8⅞ in.)

The entire object is framed by parallel ridges between which a "guilloche" is placed. The two upper corners have a petal each, the narrow end of which is punched with a hole for attachment to fabric or leather; holes are also found on the sides and bottom of the plaque. The upper register consists of mythical winged beasts confronting a "sacred tree." On the left, facing right, are first a female sphinx, then a bird-tailed lion-griffin. The "tree" is next with a lion-griffin, sphinx, and finally a third lion-griffin skillfully fitted into the narrow corner by folding its rear legs, all facing left. This register is separated by a ridge from the rest of the design which is fitted into the remaining space, in which all the figures are directed toward the lower point of the epaulette. The outer registers consist of two processions of fantastic beasts, again all winged, but with new elements. Beginning at the left we have a bull, man-headed bull, horned lion-griffin, and lion. At the right: a bull, man-headed bull, horned lion-griffin, griffin, and lion. At the point of the epaulette and on the same ground line as the right-hand procession is a winged bull, its forelegs bent to the ground. The most interesting scene of this object, and one of the most interesting in the entire Ziwiyeh repertoire, is a strange bird, its wings outspread and seen from above, but its head in profile. It grasps in its beak a human head and in its talons two tiny *Mischwesen* of an indeterminable kind: they appear to be young beasts of some sort, their heads rather resembling young caprids, but their legs and feet seem to be those of felines (or canines?). In the narrow point of this ridge-defined space a naturalistically rendered, roaring lion seems to confront the great bird with defiance.

The artistic traditions involved at Ziwiyeh are, to say the least, confusing. Scythian, Phoenician, Assyrian, Urartian, and native Persian elements abound. Some of the ivories found in the Ziwiyeh Treasure must be imports from Assyria, but others are just as certainly local products. It has been proposed to call the Treasure "Mannaean" after the textually documented inhabitants of the region, but the material from Hasanlu, less derivative and more original in style, seems to disprove the Mannaean tag. The arguments for and against these various attributions have been sufficiently well put forward in the literature cited.

BIBLIOGRAPHY: *Sept mille ans d'art en Iran* (Paris, 1961), p. 84, no. 500 A, pls. XXXVII, XXXVIII, XLI 1 (right side only then known); *BMMA* 21 (1963), p. 277, fig. 5; R. Ghirshman, *The Art of Ancient Iran* (New York, 1964), fig. 378; L. Byvanck-Quarles van Ufford, "Points de repère pour la chronologie de l'art grec au 7me siècle av. J.-C." *Bulletin van de Vereeniging tot Bevordering der Kennis van de Antieke Beschaving te 's-Gravenhage* 39 (1964), p. 69, fig. 10; "Sumptuary Arts . . ." pp. 13-14, no. 7 (ill.), from which most of the above has been quoted; Amandry and Ghirshman, *op. cit.* (in press).

54   Rhyton with Ram's Head Protome

From Kaplantu (?), North West Iran
Seventh to Sixth Century B.C.
Silver
Length: 28.5 cm (11¼ in.)

A drinking or pouring cup worked on a bitumen or other yielding core to shape the ram's head; the horns were worked separately and soldered to the main piece. The carefully and intricately worked curls are typically Persian. In earlier times they were more conventionally rendered; we might even cite the feather-pattern of No. 47 as an early example.

The decoration divides the rhyton into three distinct zones of pattern: the smooth planes of the head, the tight-ly-curled mane, and the narrow ribbing of the neck. The curling and ripple-ridged horns form a neat transition between zones. Although I have published this rhyton as Achaemenian work, it is probably earlier, despite the ear which is otherwise found only on Achaemenian animals.

BIBLIOGRAPHY: *Sept mille ans d'art en Iran* (Paris, 1961), p. 82, no. 491; *Financial Times* [London], November 1961; "The Exposition of Iranian Art in Paris," *Archaeology* 15 (1962), p. 52; R. Ghirshman in *Artibus Asiae* 25 (1962), pp. 57 ff., fig 19; "Sumptuary Arts . . ." pp. 20-21, no. 12 (ill.); *Bulletin of the Cleveland Museum of Art* 53 (1966), fig. 14 c.
Cf. Cleveland Museum of Art 63.479 and similar rhyta in The Metropolitan Museum of Art and the University Museum, Philadelphia: *BMMA* 15 (1956), pp. 9 ff. For general discussion, see R. Ghirshman, "Le rhyton en Iran," *Artibus Asiae* 25 (1962), pp. 57 ff. Amandry and Ghirshman, *op. cit.*

55 Protome of a Rhyton

Iran
About Seventh Century B.C.
Bronze
Diameter of opening: 11.5 cm (4½ in.)
Height from opening to tip of noses: 9.5 cm (3¾ in.)

The three rams' heads form what is evidently the protome
of a rhyton, which seems to have been cut away from the
upper part of the vessel. The style is rather peculiar although it is evidently Iranian. Some features, like the
heavy brows and the treatment of the hair falling between
the eyes, are reminiscent of Achaemenian workmanship
and its immediate predecessors. That the object is not
Achaemenian is obvious. Two curious elements are the
highly exaggerated tear ducts, which are unusually long,
and the muscles extending from the corners of the mouth.
These are not found in Achaemenian art or, for that
matter as far as I can tell, in any of the styles current in
Western Asia in the early first millennium B.C., although
the prominent tear duct is common on pre-Achaemenian
and Achaemenian eyes (cf. No. 54 and No. 58). Another
feature which relates the protome to vessels like No. 54
is the horizontal fluting of the rhyton which is here further detailed with hatching.

BIBLIOGRAPHY: Sale Catalogue (Luzern), *Ars Antiqua* 7 November
1964, p. 11, no. 26, pl. IX.

56 Tripod of Three Bulls

Iran, Pre-Achaemenian (?) or Early Achaemenian
About Sixth Century B.C.
Bronze
Height: 5.8 cm (2⁵⁄₁₆ in.)

The style of these bulls is related to those on the silver
vase No. 57, but the modeling and treatment of the sculpture are much more generalized. The object is possibly
explained by several long pins (unpublished) in the
Heeramaneck Collection, New York, the ends of which are
formed by umbrella-like groups of three animals or parts
of animals. These pin-heads are, however, certainly of the
Marlik Culture and earlier than the Pomerance tripod. A
hole in the center of the latter indicates that it, too, might
have been the finial of a pin. The form of the bulls with
reversed heads has its counterparts in the handles of
vases during the Achaemenian Period (No. 59). The object was perhaps made early in this period, in the last half
of the sixth century.

57 Vase with Bull Handles

Iran, Achaemenian
Late Sixth Century B.C.
Silver
Height: 16 cm (6⁵⁄₁₆ in.)

The two youthful bulls which spring upward to form the handles of this vessel have an identical mate in the Archaeological Museum, Teheran. The latter seems to have come from a somewhat differently shaped vessel to which it and its missing companion were attached. The shape of the Pomerance vase is unusual.

BIBLIOGRAPHY: *Sept mille ans d'art en Iran* (Paris, 1961), p. 50, no. 283; *Kunst-Schätze aus Iran* (Zurich, 1962), p. 60, no. 131, pl. 29; *7000 Anni d'Arte Iranica* (Milan, 1963), no. 172, pl. 27; *7000 Jahre Kunst in Iran* (Essen, 1962), p. 76, no. 132; *7000 Jaar Perzische Kunst* (The Hague, 1962), pl. 14; *ILN* 27 December 1958, p. 1141, fig. 12; Culican, *op. cit.*, fig. 12; "Sumptuary Arts . . ." pp. 15-16, no. 9 (ill.), with fuller discussion.
Cf. the Teheran bull handle: *7000 Years of Iranian Art* (Washington, 1964), p. 87, no. 447.

58 Plate with Four Young Bulls

Iran, Achaemenian, perhaps from Egypt
About 525 B.C.
Silver
Diameter: 32 cm (12⁵⁄₈ in.)

This remarkable and very beautiful plate was probably made in the same atelier as the silver plate with four ibexes now in the Schimmel Collection. Four bulls leap counterclockwise, their hooves touching a raised band around the rim, their horns, ears and tails touching another raised band which encloses a rosette made up of sixteen petals encircling a slightly raised boss. It has not been possible to examine the plate under the microscope, but almost certainly the relief of the animals was produced by swedging away the background. Details are added by chasing. The plate was perhaps part of the royal tableware or temple service. The curvilinear style is preeminently Achaemenian. A sweeping curve may be drawn along the back of one bull, continued through the next and so on until it returns to the first. This same line may be interrupted on any bull, to recurve through the tail until it comes to the tip of the horn, when it returns again. The elliptical modeling of the shoulders is echoed in the curving lines of the breast and the stomach. In fact, straight lines are almost nonexistent. Some circumstantial evidence exists for an Egyptian origin of the two plates, and it is doubtful that the work of the pre-Achaemenian inhabitants of the mountains of North West Iran could have found its way to Egypt except through devious routes. On the other hand, it is not impossible that the Achaemenian conquest of Egypt in 525 B.C. brought with it objects from the royal treasury, either of contemporary or even earlier manufacture. Occasional finds of Persian art have been made in Egypt and prove that purely Achaemenian work was imported.

BIBLIOGRAPHY: "Sumptuary Arts . . ." pp. 17-19, no. 10 (ill.), from which most of the above has been quoted; *ibid.*, no. 11 for the Schimmel plate with bibliography and discussion; Amandry and Ghirshman, *op. cit.*

59   Amphora with Ibex Handles

Achaemenian, found in Iraq
Fifth Century B.C.
Silver
Height of vase: 28 cm (11 in.); with handles, 33 cm
   (13 in.)

Two holes on either side of the base indicate that liquid
was poured through this vessel into others. The vase has a
remarkable history: it was acquired and first exhibited
without its handles and admired for its beautiful shape.
Some years later, the handles, presumably separated from
their vessel by the discoverers and divided as loot, were
acquired by Mr. Pomerance, who was able to rejoin the
long-separated elements. This was indeed a fortunate oc-
currence because the vessel with its handles is unquestion-
ably the finest of its type preserved. The ibex handles are
superb examples of classical Achaemenian style which, at
its best, is an art of careful refinement and reserve.

   It is interesting to note that the vessel was found in Iraq,
one of the satrapies of the Achaemenian Empire.

   Among the tribute being brought forward to the Great
King in the reliefs of the Apadana at Persepolis, are
several amphoras with animal handles.

BIBLIOGRAPHY: *Sept mille ans d'art en Iran*, p. 115, no. 685 (without
handles) ; "Sumptuary Arts . . ." pp. 25-27, no. 15 (ill.), from which
most of the above has been taken; Amandry and Ghirshman, *op. cit.*;
Amandry has collected most of the preserved examples in the article
cited, and we can now add this splendid vessel in the Pomerance
Collection.
Cf. for amphoras in the Apadana reliefs, see good illustrations,
Amandry in *Antike Kunst* 2 (1959), pl. 20, 1, 2.

60 Median Servant

Persepolis, probably from the Western Stairway of the
    Palace of Xerxes, east face of the parapet of the
    southern flight.
Fifth Century B.C.
Limestone
Height: 35.6 cm (14 in.)   Width: 19.5 cm ($7^{11}\!/_{16}$ in.)

One of the noblest monuments of antiquity was the great
royal city of Persepolis in the Plain of Fars where the
Achaemenid rulers of Persia established their sacred
capital. Although sadly mutilated through the centuries,
it remains the most completely preserved city of the
ancient world. Only Athens is comparable.

    Founded by Darius, called the Great, the city was
furbished by his successors, particularly Xerxes. It is from
the palace of this king, who unsuccessfully tried to con-
quer Greece, that the relief here pictured probably comes.
All that remains is the torso and head of one of the
innumerable Median servants who, with their Achaemenian counterparts, eternally mount the stairways of the
Persepolis palaces, bearing offerings to their king. The
bashlyk, or cap, he wears is thought to have been made of
felt; he probably carries a covered dish in his hands.

BIBLIOGRAPHY: Queens College Catalogue, pp. 14 and 31, no. 19 (ill.).
For the reliefs of Persepolis, see E. F. Schmidt, *Persepolis* I, *passim*
and especially pl. 163 B-D for the probable origin of this relief. See
also the indispensable review of *Persepolis* I by R. D. Barnett in *Iraq*
19 (1957), pp. 55 ff.

61 Persian Guard

Persepolis, perhaps from Eastern Stairway of the Palace
    of Xerxes
Fifth Century B.C.
Limestone
Height: 54.7 cm (21 9/16 in.)

Although the original location of this fragment is a
mystery, its subject is not. Throughout the buildings at
Persepolis, the royal guard is shown standing at attention,
frequently armed with lance, bow, and quiver, although
in this case the bow is missing. So frequent is the occur-
rence of these upright figures, that one is reminded at
once of the Ten Thousand Immortals, the elite corps of
the Achaemenian troops. Each wears, as shown on the
reliefs, a tall, fluted helmet called the *cidaris* and a long
flowing robe referred to by Herodotus (VII:61) as
"sleeved tunics of divers colors." It is interesting that the
peaceful, even relaxed stance of these warriors makes no
reflection of the wars being fought in the expansion and
consolidation of the empire of the Achaemenids. It is now
thought that Persepolis was established as a sacred com-
pound in which to celebrate the annual New Year's
Festival, even today the great event of the Iranian year.

For possible location of this relief, cf. *Persepolis* I, pl. 173 C.

62 Animal Contest

Ordos
Second to First Century B.C.
Bronze
Height: 7.3 cm (2⅞ in.)   Length: 12 cm (4¾ in.)

A feline attacks a fallen ibex(?), and a bird of prey attacks the feline while it is clutching the ibex with its talons.

About the turn of the century a Russian archaeologist, Talko-Hryncewicz, found near Troickosavask (which is close to Lake Baikal on the Russian-Mongolian border) a bronze plaque which is the duplicate of No. 62 except that it faces in the other direction. In 1932 the Swedish anthropologist, J. G. Andersson, published a long and interesting article based on the collection of Ordos bronzes in the Museum of Far Eastern Antiquities in Stockholm. He published in that article a bronze plaque almost identical to the one found by Talko-Hryncewicz. Andersson's plaque was, apparently, in a curio shop in Peiping in 1932. In 1934 Joachim Werner published an article dealing with the Ordos bronze question and included the Troickosavask and Andersson plaques, as well as the right half of still another identical plaque then in the Loo Collection. From the photographs published by Werner, it is impossible to tell whether or not the three plaques are actually one in various stages of cleaning and preservation.

The context of Talko-Hryncewicz's find gave a *terminus post quem* of 118 B.C. for his plaque. In some way unknown to us, the Pomerance plaque must have come from this same find and is to be dated similarly. The use of the plaques is uncertain, but they perhaps adorned a belt or the like. It is interesting to note that, while having some of the features of Scythian work (namely the closely interwoven design and the curving forms and decorative additions), the Ordos bronzes are closer to an organically modeled style.

Cf. J. Werner, "Zur Stellung der Ordosbronzen," *Eurasia Septentrionalis Antiqua* 9 (Helsinki, 1934), pp. 261 ff. and figs. 5-7 for parallel plaques and bibliography; J. G. Andersson, "Hunting Magic in the Animal Style," *Bulletin of the Museum of Far Eastern Antiquities* 4 (Stockholm, 1932), pp. 301 ff., and pl. 33, 1.

63 Standing Man

South Arabia, Sabaean
Second to Third Century A.D.
Alabaster
Height: 26.8 cm (10%⁄₁₆ in.)

The Sabaean kingdom of South Arabia in the first centuries after Christ is still little understood. Its sculpture is a strange mixture of naturalism and stylized abstraction which may be quite appealing, as in this example. In contrast to the ludicrous mannerism of the legs, the torso and parts of the face are treated with some realism.

Cf. *AJA* 38 (1934), p. 331, fig. 1.

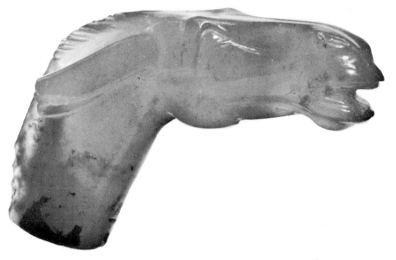

64 Head of a Horse

Roman Egypt (?)
Chalcedony
Length: 6 cm (2⅜ in.)

There are two holes going straight up into the thickest part of the neck; part of a bronze pin is still preserved in one hole.

The head is finely modeled in such a way as to give it a strong feeling of vigorous liveliness. Although quite small, it seems evident from the sharp angle between head and neck that the object is probably a handle. Its period is uncertain, but since its supposed provenance is Egypt, a Roman date seems the likeliest possibility.

ANCIENT EGYPTIAN ART

Bernard V. Bothmer

65   Cosmetic Palette

Late Predynastic Period, about 3400-3200 B.C.
Schist (metamorphic slate)
Height: 11.5 cm (4⅝₆ in.)   Length: 20 cm (7⅞ in.)

The custom of providing the deceased in his grave with
the slate palette on which he used to grind his ritual eye
make-up in real life goes back to the beginning of the
Predynastic Period of ancient Egypt, about 4000 B.C. In
early times, these palettes were mainly of geometric shape,
oval, rhomboid or rectangular; in the course of the fourth
millennium B.C. they were more and more copiously
adorned both with animal heads and with the outlines of
complete animals. Although contours and interior design
were usually very simple, the eye was often inlaid, and
frequently a hole was added for suspension.

For palettes in form of a fish, see J. Vandier, *Manuel d'archéologie
égyptienne* I (1952), pp. 382-384.

66   Ointment Dish

New Kingdom, Dynasty XVIII, Fifteenth to Fourteenth
        Century B.C.
Steatite
Height: 7 cm (2¾ in.)   Width: 11.5 cm (4½ in.)

Bound antelope as a game delicacy have been represented in Egyptian relief since the Old Kingdom, but only
with the New Kingdom (after 1600 B.C.) does the motif
appear partly in the round, as ointment dishes and as
so-called toilet spoons which served as mixing bowls for
sweet-smelling cosmetic salves and skin tonics.

The reverse of this dish is hollow; the obverse shows
the likeness of the animal both in modeling and in engraved design, for which the dark soft stone has been
employed with much skill.

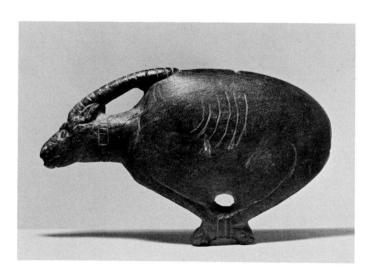

For similar pieces, see F. W. von Bissing, *Steingefässe—Catalogue
général des antiquités égyptiennes du Musée du Caire*, nos. 18065-
18793 (Vienna, 1904), p. 110, no. 18544, pl. VIII. William C. Hayes,
The Scepter of Egypt II (Cambridge, Mass., 1959), p. 191, fig.
106 (upper right, MMA 30.8.84, from the collection of Theodore M.
Davis).

67   Faience Bowl

Said to have been found at Tell el Amarna
New Kingdom, Dynasty XVIII, Fourteenth Century B.C.
Blue faience, with black manganese design
Height: 7.5 cm ($2^{15}/_{16}$ in.)   Diam.: 20 cm ($7^{7}/_{8}$ in.)

Within the confines of the bowl's rim, a design of lotus
flowers and buds has been arranged nearly symmetrically
and yet not too precisely, so that the floating quality of
water flora has been subtly expressed. The decoration al-
ludes both to the flower-filled bowls which the Egyptians
displayed in offering and banquet scenes and to the lily
ponds which formed an essential part of the luxurious
villas of the XVIIIth Dynasty.

BIBLIOGRAPHY: Queens College Catalogue, p. 20, no. 107.
   A similar, but larger piece in Berlin (19800) is illustrated in H.
Schaefer & W. Andrae, *Die Kunst des Alten Orients* (Berlin, 1925,
1930, 1942): 1st ed., fig. 396,2; 2d and 3d eds., fig. 412,1.

68   Head of a Queen

From Hermopolis Magna, originally from Amarna
New Kingdom, Dynasty XVIII, about 1360 B.C.
Limestone with traces of paint (most of the polychromy is
    modern)
Height: 21.5 cm (8½ in.)   Width: 26.3 cm (10⅜ in.)

This royal personage, identified as such by the uraeus above the forehead, holds in the raised hand a sistrum, a ritual rattle which is always carried by women but never by men. The two hands above emanate from the rays of the Aten, the living sun disk, the one God of the Amarna Period; one of these passes behind the Queen's uraeus, whereas the other holds the sign of life, a somewhat distorted *ankh* not uncommon in this period. The Queen wears a valanced double wig and a large disk earring; in addition to the sistrum, she holds a streamer or sash in her raised hand. There was a column of inscription behind her head. At the right-hand edge of the block, the outline of a leading figure appears. The delicate features distinctly differ from those of the famous Queen of the Amarna age, Nefertiti, whose face is far more drawn and haggard; thus, this must be a younger queen of her succession, probably her daughter Merit-aten, wife of Semenkh-ka-ra (1364-1361 B.C.).

BIBLIOGRAPHY: John D. Cooney, *Amarna Reliefs from Hermopolis in American Collections* (Brooklyn, 1965), pp. 26-27, no. 15 (ill.). For the same wig worn by a male attendant, see the figure in the relief no. 35, page 59, of Cooney, *op. cit.* The distorted *ankh* sign, added almost as an afterthought, is often found in Amarna reliefs both from Amarna and from Karnak; see *Revue de l'Égypte ancienne* 2 (1929), pl. IV, and Brooklyn 64.199.2: *The Brooklyn Museum Annual* VI (1964-65), p. 17 (ill.).

69   Calf and Keeper

From Hermopolis Magna, originally from Amarna
New Kingdom, Dynasty XVIII, about 1365 B.C.
Limestone (repainted in modern times)
Height: 22.6 cm (8⅞ in.)   Width: 52.1 cm (20½ in.)

In well-modeled, deeply sunk relief, a bull calf is represented being led by an attendant—either to be sacrificed or to be shown in a procession of tributes. The slightly opened mouth of the animal, the creases of the skin round the eye, the relief layers of near ear in front of far ear in front of the heavily pleated garment of the attendant: all these features mark the lively style of the Amarna Period.

BIBLIOGRAPHY: J. D. Cooney, *op. cit.*, pp. 58-59, no. 36 (ill.).

70   Companion of the Dead

Third Intermediate Period, Dynasty XXI, 1085-945 B.C.
Blue faience with black manganese design
Height: 11 cm (4⁵⁄₁₆ in.)

The custom of placing mummiform "servants" in the
tombs of great persons of ancient Egypt persisted from the
Middle Kingdom (about 2000 B.C.) to the middle of the
Ptolemaic Period (about 200 B.C.). The underlying concept was that the deceased should have a ready substitute
when called upon to do farm labor in the nether world.
Depending on the means of the person thus provided for,
such substitutes—called shawabtis—were fashioned in
large numbers from stone and wood, and especially in
faience.

This shawabti was made for a man named Djed-khonsu-
iuf-ankh, identified by the inscription on the front of the
figure. But the piece itself was not made especially for
him personally; it had been made as a stock figure that
could be labeled for a woman as well as for a man. The
two hands hold hoes, still today the standard tool of the
farm laborer; neatly painted on the back is a basket for
seeds.

For the type of shawabti under discussion, see Flinders Petrie,
Shabtis (London, 1935), pl. XXXVII.

71   Offering Bearer

Late Period, Dynasties XXVII-XXX, about 500-350 B.C.
Bronze
Height: 16 cm (6⁵⁄₁₆ in.)

Statuettes of men presenting offerings to a god are not
uncommon in the Late Period, when they are usually combined with the figure of the diety, worshipped by the
donor, the figures usually mounted on a single base. Our
man with the tray on his head is lacking his feet; the
figure probably was broken off the base which bore the
image of the god.

The tray, which is laden with a pyramid of round
cakes, is steadied on the man's head with the fingertips of
both hands. The close-cropped hair is well outlined; the
features are idealized. In contrast to the arms and legs, the
torso is modeled with much detail where it is not covered
by the tripartite short skirt.

BIBLIOGRAPHY: Wilhelm Spiegelberg, "A Bronze Statue of a Cake-
Carrier," *Journal of Egyptian Archaeology* 16 (1930), p. 73, pl.
XVIII.
Cf. G. Roeder, *Ägyptische Bronzefiguren* (Berlin, 1956), p. 304, par.
374.

72 God Ptah with Worshipers

Late Period, probably Dynasty XXVI, about 550 B.C.
Bronze, partly gold-inlaid
Height: 24 cm (9⁷⁄₁₆ in.)   Width of base: 6 cm (2⅜ in.)
Depth of base: 13.5 cm (5⁵⁄₁₆ in.)

The close-fitting gold cap and mummy-like shroud char-
acterize the main figure as that of the god Ptah of
Memphis, who is shown here with ceremonial beard,
broad collar, and multiple scepter, standing on a pedestal
which in turn rests on a flat base. A kneeling worshiper
with offering table rests on the pedestal, facing the god;
a second worshiper (presumably the same donor)
kneels on the base, also facing Ptah and presenting a vase.
Eyebrows, eyes, and beardstrap were formerly inlaid;
they are now empty but there are gold wire decorations
in the collar and the beard. The god holds a combination
scepter of *ankh, was,* and *djed,* divine symbols of life and
stability; the scepter closely follows the modeling of the
torso.

The pedestal bears on both sides engraved *ankh, was,*
and *neb* signs, and the beveled front is decorated with the
Upper and Lower Egyptian genii of abundance and their
offerings.

BIBLIOGRAPHY: Daninos Pacha, *Collection d'antiquités égyptiennes
de Tigrane Pacha d'Abro* (Paris, 1911), p. 5, no. 12, pl. XI.
For bronze figures of the God Ptah in general, see G. Roeder,
op. cit., pp. 195 ff.; for groups with donor figures, *ibid.,* pp. 505 ff.

ANCIENT GREEK ART

Compiled by Jean L. Keith
Contributors, G.M.A. Hanfmann and
David G. Mitten

73 Flat Idol

Probably from Asia Minor
About 2500-2000 B.C.
Marble
Height: 24.2 cm (9½ in.)

These stylized figures, commonly called idols, carved
from a thin slab of marble, are frequently found throughout Western Anatolia in graves of the Early Bronze Age
people in the second half of the third millennium B.C.
They are often referred to as "Yortan" figurines, from the
cemetery near Balikesir where the first examples were
found. The design, a highly abstract bust with a circular
head crowning a semicircular or square body, is closely
related to that of the more schematic Cycladic figures
of violin shape (compare No. 74). It now appears that
manufacture of schematized marble figurines, usually
female, was a trait widely diffused throughout the Aegean
basin and its borderlands during the Early Bronze Age.

Cf. a number of figurines similar to the Pomerance piece found in
pithos burials at Karatas in Lycia, see M. Mellink, "Excavations at
Karatas-Semayük in Lycia, 1963," *AJA* 68 (1964), p. 277, pl. 82,
figs. 24-25, for an up-to-date discussion of the distribution of these
idols. Three idols of the same form from the Ionian coast are
illustrated in C. Zervos, *L'Art des Cyclades* (Paris, 1957), fig. 52.
(DGM) Compare also the idol in Sale Catalogue (London), *Sotheby*,
28 June 1965, p. 10, no. 21 (ill.).

74 Statuette of Violin Type

Cycladic
Third Millennium B.C.
Marble
Height: 22.6 cm (8⅞ in.)

A head of the familiar type, with raised vertical nose
ridge, sits atop a long neck. The axe-shaped body is deline-
ated by deep notches at the waist, forming stubby projections for the arms. Holes or perforations at the neck
are unusual in Cycladic figures and may be intended for
suspension or here required by the repair, which may
have been made in ancient times. (DGM)

Cf. C. Zervos, *ibid.*, for a similar piece, without head, p. 83, fig. 58,
lower right; perforations in approximately the same locations as on
the Pomerance piece appear in the object shown on p. 81, fig. 56,
bottom center. A figure of less rounded proportions appears in
Antike Kunst 8 (1965), pl. 17, 2.

75 Statuette

Cycladic
Third Millennium B.C.
Marble with dark rust-colored incrustation
Height: 19.5 cm (7¾ in.)

Many female idols of this type have come from the Cycladic Islands in the Aegean Sea and neighboring areas. Within a basic convention which includes the arms attached to the body and crossed under the breast, the slightly flexed legs grooved front and back and the schematic head, a surprisingly wide variation in proportions and details was possible. The actual purpose of these figures, which vary in height from a few inches to nearly three feet, is not certain; they may represent a goddess or an attendant.

The U-shaped head is flat on the top edge. Breaks at the neck and above the left and below the right knees have been mended. A large chip from below the right shoulder to the right buttock has been broken away. The legs are separated from just above the knees to the heels, where they join again.

Cf. Cycladic idols of this type in C. Zervos, *ibid.*, p. 78, pl. 50 b-c. F. N. Pryce, *Catalogue of Sculpture in the Department of Greek and Roman Antiquities of the British Museum* I, pt. 1 (London, 1928), pp. 3-13, presents others of the type. *Antike Kunst* 8 (1965), pp. 59-90, includes three articles on the meaning, interpretation and archaeology of Cycladic finds.

76 Head

Cycladic
Said to be Third Millennium B.C.
White crystalline marble
Height: 6.1 cm (2⁷⁄₁₆ in.)

The small head is of the type that comes from female idols like the preceding, No. 75. A most unusual feature of this head is its nearly perfect oval shape. Most of these heads are U-shaped, straight across the top and slightly rolled over at the back. (DGM)

A heavy, dark rust-colored incrustation covers most of the head.

77   Pyxis with Lid

Minoan
2000-1900 B.C.
Hard black-speckled pale gray-green stone
Height: 4.8 cm (1⅞ in.)   Diameter: 9.9 cm ($3^{15}/_{16}$ in.)

From very early times, small vessels with lids were used
for precious materials such as ointments, perfumes and
cosmetics or, in larger sizes, to hold jewelry or toilet
articles. These were called pyxides by the Greeks, but jars
of fine stone were used in Predynastic and Old Kingdom
Egypt for similar purposes, and perhaps provided the
inspiration for Minoan craftsmen.

This pyxis has a raised lip and is neatly mended from
two large fragments; the lid is intact.

BIBLIOGRAPHY: Sale Catalogue (London), *Sotheby*, 11 April 1960, p.
29, no. 142 (ill.). Cf. discussion of early Minoan stone vessels in R. A.
Seager, *Explorations in the Island of Mochlos* (Boston and New
York, 1912), pp. 99-104, pl. I-VII. The Minoan vases seem generally
to have been made from softer stones: steatite, decorative marbles,
alabaster and breccias. (DGM) C. Zervos, *L'Art de la Crète* (Paris,
1956), illustrates several squat stone jars, figs. 148, 154, 160-162, 164,
170, and particularly 166 which includes a vessel from Mochlos similar to our pyxis.

78 Fantastic Animal

Minoan
Late Minoan III, about 1400 B.C.
Pink-buff terracotta
Height: 22.5 cm (8⅞ in.)

A mythological beast of uncertain species, this great-eyed creature finds his closest kin among the plastic vases and elaborate terracotta figurines, some of them very large, which populate the world of Late Minoan III decoration. Mr. Pomerance has pointed to the resemblance of this beast to one of an earlier time which carries a goddess riding sidesaddle on a lentoid sealstone from the *dromos* (entry corridor) of the Treasury of Clytemnestra at Mycenae. (DGM)

A whitish residue or slip has been worn away on the back, the haunches and "jaws" of the animal's head. Traces of dark red are seen on the belly. There is a small hole beneath the tail.

BIBLIOGRAPHY: University of Pennsylvania Catalogue, no. 7.
For Middle Minoan plastic vases and figures, see C. Zervos, *ibid.*, pp. 220, 222-225, figs. 279-280, 282-289. The seal from Mycenae with the marvelous beast is discussed by G. Mylonas, *Ancient Mycenae* (Princeton, 1959), p. 95, fig. 35. It is also discussed by E. T. Vermeule in *The Classical Journal* 54 (1958), no. 3, p. 107, fig. 12.

79 Beaked Jug

Mycenaean
About 1450-1425 B.C.
Terracotta
Height: 27.0 cm (10⅝ in.)

This type of pitcher was usually decorated with aquatic motifs. Created during the Mycenaean IIB or IIIA period, it is similar to a ewer from Salamis in the Fogg Art Museum, Cambridge (1959.123). The shape may have antecedents in metal vessels, as does No. 80, a storage jar.

The shoulder is decorated with parallel chevrons, argonauts with papyrus derivatives, and quirks. The chevrons and the swastika-like quirks are geometric forms, while the other ornaments are stylized representations of marine animal and plant life. Both the base and the top of the handle are pierced with diagonal holes. Part of the beak and some of the painting are restored.

BIBLIOGRAPHY: Queens College Catalogue, pp. 23 and 57, no. 161 (ill.) ; *Ancient Art*, p. 23, no. 99, pls. 26, 31.
Cf. the Fogg Museum piece, *AJA* 54 (1950), pl. 1, 5, and *Ancient Art in American Private Collections*, p. 26, no. 133, pl. XXXVI. On that vase, however, the neck is encircled by stripes, not hanging petals as in the Pomerance jug, and chevrons, quirks and stripes around the body are absent. (DGM)
For identification of shape and decorative motifs, see Arne Furumark, *The Mycenaean Pottery* (Stockholm, 1940-1941), shape: p. 30, fig. 5, n. 144; papyrus: p. 265, fig. 34, motif 11, no. 6; argonaut: pp. 306-7, fig. 50, motif 22, no. 7, 9 and others; quirk: p. 360, fig. 61, motif 48, no. 1; parallel chevrons: p. 383, fig. 67, motif 58, no. 3.

80 Three-handled Jar

Beginning of Late Mycenaean III, about 1425-1400 B.C.
Yellowish-white clay, brown painting
Height: 21 cm (8¼ in.)

The pear shape of this vase as well as the scale pattern on its shoulder is of Minoan origin, developing in Crete from a variety of large and small pithoid storage jars. Their relationship to earlier metal vessels is demonstrated here by the flattened handles and their manner of attachment, and by the painted rings circling the base of the neck which reflect the tubular ring covering the junction of neck and jar in metal jugs.

The jar is neatly repaired from several large fragments, with few restorations.

BIBLIOGRAPHY: André Emmerich Gallery, Inc., *Early Art in Greece* (New York, 1965), p. 29, no. 79 (ill.) and further comparative material and classification according to A. Furumark, *ibid.*
Cf. a pithoid jar of a shape similar but narrower toward the base in the Metropolitan Museum of Art (74.51.764), from Cyprus. Its scale- and ring-painting is less regular than that of the Pomerance jar, and its handles are round in section and placed horizontally on the shoulder. Another jar very similar in shape is in the British Museum (H 197), from Tomb 26 in Ialysos, Rhodes: *CVA*, British Museum, Fasc. 5, III A, pl. 1, 25. The fact that scale patterns on three-handled pithoid and other pottery shapes have been excavated near Pylos in the Peloponnesus indicates the wide spread of designs and vessels of this sort throughout the Late Mycenaean Mediterranean world; F. Schachermeyr, *AA* (1962), cols. 275 ff., figs. 53-54, describes finds from the Rutsi II tholos tomb brought to light by S. Marinatos. In the Pomerance Collection is another Mycenaean pottery vessel of metallic origin, No. 79.

81   Fragment of a Sarcophagus

Mycenaean
About 1300-1100 B.C.
Terracotta
Height: 33.3 cm (13⅛ in.)
Width: 33.4 cm (13⁵⁄₃₂ in.)

Terracotta chests used for sepulchral purposes, *larnakes,* were often decorated and usually with scenes appropriate to their purpose. On this Mycenaean *larnax,* two of a group of women commiserate, their arms upraised in a traditional mourning gesture.

BIBLIOGRAPHY: *Ancient Art*, p. 23, no. 102, pls. 26, 31; University of Pennsylvania Catalogue, no. 6; E. T. Vermeule, *Greece in the Bronze Age* (Chicago, 1964), pp. 212, 343, n. 13, fig. 37a; *id.*, "Painted Mycenaean Larnakes" *JHS* 85 (1965), pp. 129 ff, no. 4, pl. XXVII c; S. E. Iakovides, "A Mycenaean Mourning Custom" *AJA* 70 (1966), pp. 46, 48.
In *Greece in the Bronze Age*, pp. 210 ff., pls. XXXIV, XXXV, Mrs. Vermeule discusses the function and decoration of the *larnakes,* and lists several examples of the type. In her more recent *JHS* article (pp. 123-148, pls. XXV-XXVIII), her study is extended and includes thirteen Mycenaean *larnakes* or fragments thereof, discussing painting style and subjects. A. H. S. Megaw refers to sites where vessels of this type have been found recently in "Archaeology in Greece, 1964-65," *Archaeological Report* (The British School in Athens, 1965) pp. 16 and 28.

82 Lyre Player

Cypriot
About 500 B.C.
Terracotta
Height: 12.5 cm (4¹⁵⁄₁₆ in.)

The musician with his head thrown back seems absorbed in the sounds he makes. He would be a good companion for the tambourine player in the Metropolitan Museum of Art (74.51.1675) who wears a "button" wreath.

The little figure, probably from Cyprus, is solid, apparently hand formed, with a depression inside the bottom flare of his skirt. His double-strand wreath is broken away over the right ear. Between his shoulder blades a small, blunt "hook" of clay points upward.

The New York piece is illustrated in Cesnola, *Atlas* II, pl. XL. Male and female musicians, in both terracotta and limestone, play flutes, citharae and harps: Cesnola, *op. cit.*, XX, pt. I, pl. XII; Vol. II, pl. V, 27, 29, 32, 37, 38; and on pls. VI and VII. J. Young, *Terracotta Figurines from Kourion in Cyprus* (University Museum Monographs, Philadelphia, 1955), includes similar excavated pieces: "Solid Votaries" are discussed and catalogued, pp. 28-38; lyre players nos. 562-564 are described on p. 33. A double fillet similar to ours is illustrated on p. 30, fig. 3, no. 7.

83 Goddess or Worshiper

Cypriot
Fifth Century B.C.
Limestone
Height: 26.2 cm (10⁵⁄₁₆ in.)

Cyprus is one of the largest islands in the Mediterranean, and its position in the eastern end of that sea made it early a focus for colonization. First settled by the Phoenicians and later by the Greeks, it was famous in the ancient world for its beauty, its wealth (particularly in copper, the name for which supposedly comes from that of the island), and its distinction as the birthplace and favorite home of Aphrodite, Greek goddess of love. Votive figures of all shapes and sizes were dedicated to the famous goddess, and this torso is possibly one. The lady may have held a lotus flower, and her himation, or cloak, exposes one shoulder in the manner of the Greek *korai*, or maidens, and the chiton, or long tunic, she wears under her cloak. On her head is a *stephanos*, or low crown.

The hair hangs long in back with four strands on each side of a central part; short horizontal gouges give a zigzag effect which is more pronounced toward the ears which are large and flat, not modeled. Whatever she held in her right hand is broken away. There are some areas of discoloration, and the stone appears white in some chipped areas, pink in others. Part of the back of the head and hair on the right have been restored.

Cf., in the large collection of Cypriot finds that came to the Metropolitan Museum of Art in New York through Luigi P. di Cesnola (74.51.2547), a small limestone statuette of a woman holding a flower in one hand and the skirt of her garment in the other. She is recorded in Cesnola *Atlas* I, pl. LVII, 382.

84 Woman's Head

Cypriot
Fifth Century B.C.
Limestone
Height: 10.7 cm (4¼ in.)

The lady wears a *sakkos*, or headcloth, which covers up her back hair, and a wreath of seven rosettes across the forehead.

There appear to be traces of red paint on the lips, and thin stripes around the neck. The ears are not visible, covered by a roll of hair above and hexafoil rosettes below. The forehead hair is modeled in a fashion similar to the back hair of the previous figure, No. 83.

BIBLIOGRAPHY: University of Pennsylvania Catalogue, no. 8, where it is dated to the sixth century B.C.
Cf. specific aspects of this little head appear on other Cypriot figures, both male and female, many now in the Metropolitan Museum of Art. The Cesnola *Atlas* includes several figures of musicians and votaries with similar characteristics; for example, the female lyre player with the pointed headdress, Vol. I, pl. LXVII, no. 441.

85 Head of a Votary

Cypriot
Second Quarter of the Fifth Century B.C.
Limestone
Height: 32.0 cm (12⅝ in.)

The full-bearded man wears two wreaths: a crown of laurel leaves above and two rows of acorns below. The rendering of the crown hair and the arrangement of forehead hair in parallel rows of corkscrew curls are reminiscent of the herm head of the Alcamenean type, No. 86 of this catalogue for an example.

The head has been broken off at the base of the neck; a trace of drapery remains at back, bottom right. A few beard curls have been replaced. The hair flows from a low crown to the back band of the wreath and forms tight sausage curls across the nape of the neck.

BIBLIOGRAPHY: *Ancient Art*, p. 25, no. 106, pl. 32.
Cf. in addition to the London head cited therein, a similar head of a votary in the Toledo Museum of Art (58.15), illustrated on the cover of *The Art Quarterly* 22 (1959). Individual elements of the Pomerance head appear in several of the Cypriot pieces in the Metropolitan Museum of Art; i.e. eyes (74.51.2826) and a beard (74.51.2462).

86   Head of Herm

Roman Copy of a Greek Fifth Century Original
White crystalline marble
Height: 20.2 cm (8 in.)

The head is most likely a copy of the famous Hermes Propylaios, "Hermes before the Gates," set up at the entrance to the Acropolis of Athens. This renowned Hermes has been attributed to Alkamenes and was copied profusely for years. A "herm" is a quadrangular shaft or pillar which is surmounted by a head or bust, or in later times by a human torso. Often phallic, the shafts were sometimes inscribed and generally had small rectangular projections at shoulder level. Herms (the name derived from the god Hermes to whom the earliest were dedicated) were set up at crossroads, at doorways, in markets; the form was used for portraits of distinguished men as well as representations of other gods.

The head has been broken off the neck diagonally from behind the beard to below the fillet that binds the hair in back; the break appears to have been smoothed off. Some white incrustation is seen in crevices. Long side locks that fell onto the shoulders have also been broken away above the earlobes.

BIBLIOGRAPHY: Queens College Catalogue, pp. 20 and 45, no. 115 (ill.).
Cf. Copies of the Alcamenean Hermes Propylaios abound dating from the fifth century to the archaizing years of the first century. The problem of these many copies is discussed by J. R. McCredie, *AJA* 66 (1962), pp. 187-189, pl. 56. Two of these copies are in the Fogg Art Museum (1960.463 and 1932.56.115). Another is in the Museum of Fine Arts, Boston; see C. C. Vermeule III, *AJA* 68 (1964), p. 324, pl. 97, fig. 2. Still others are in the Metropolitan Museum; see G. M. A. Richter, *Catalogue of Greek Sculptures in the Metropolitan Museum of Art* (Cambridge, Mass. 1954), 03.12.3 (G.R. 1069), pp. 35-6, no. 48, pl. XLIII, a, b; 03.12.4 (G.R. 1070), p. 36, no. 49, pl. XLIV, a-c; 19.192.69, p. 36, no. 50, pl. XLIII, c-e.

87   Torso of Aphrodite

Said to have been found in the Gulf of Taranto
Late Fourth to Third Century B.C.
Marble
Height: 28 cm (11 in.)

The enormously popular "Venus Pudica" motif was
varied in a number of subtypes. Here the marked bending
of the upper part, the arms held off from the body, the
straight vertical of the spine and the turn of the head to
her left suggest a closer relation to the prototype, Prax-
iteles' Cnidia, and to such variants on it as the bronze
statue in the Metropolitan Museum (12.173) rather than
the "impregnable" Capitoline type or the late Hellenistic
Medici type, which seems less slender. The treatment of
the back is remarkably realistic and sophisticated.

It has been suggested that the front surface has been
worn by sea and sand. There is some slight golden yellow
discoloration around the left leg and at the broken surfaces of the thighs.

Cf. M. Bieber, *Sculpture of the Hellenistic Age* (rev. ed., New York,
1961), Cnidian types figs. 24-27; C. Blinkenberg, *Knidia* (Copenhagen, 1933), figs. 10, 60 f.; pls. 10, 14 for her back. For the Medici
type, C. Alexander in *BMMA* 11 (1953), pp. 241-250; G. Mansuelli,
Galleria degli Uffizi, Le Sculture 1, (Rome, 1958), nos. 45, 89, 138;
C. D. Caskey, *Catalogue of Greek and Roman Sculpture* (Boston,
1925), no. 80, pp. 156-158, ill. on p. 157. (GMAH) A small torso of
the Capitoline type can be seen in the Metropolitan Museum of Art
(21.88.70) labeled as a "reduced [in size] Roman copy of a lost
Greek work of the late fourth century B.C." Other examples are
illustrated in Bieber, *op. cit.*, figs. 34-35.

88   Head of a Woman

Perhaps a Roman Copy of a Greek Fifth Century Type
Marble
Height: 19.1 cm (7½ in.)

The reflective expression of the head suggests that its
prototypes may be Attic grave reliefs of the fifth century.
A fragment of such a stele in the Metropolitan Museum
(30.11.3) represents a mourning woman with head turned
to the right and eyes downcast. There, a narrow band en-
circles the head at least two times, and the back of the
head is veiled where it merges into the ground of the
relief.

The front top of the Pomerance head is worn in two
areas and over the right ear as well. The band that winds
around the head seems to be a wide one, gathered to make
it narrower.

BIBLIOGRAPHY: Queens College Catalogue, pp. 20, 44, no. 114 (ill.).

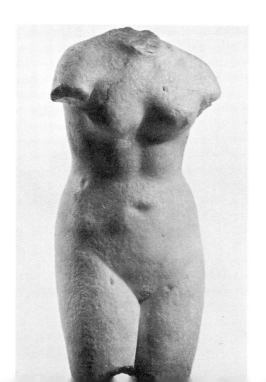

89 Seated Man

Probably Northern Greek (Thessaly or Macedonia)
Eighth or Early Seventh Century B.C.
Bronze, with pale green patina on body
Height: 3.2 cm (1¼ in.)

While tiny statuettes like this little man are sometimes called "drinkers" or "flute players," the fact is that we do not know what they are doing. The oval base with two partly circular cuts is like a Boeotian shield in shape; many small northern Greek Geometric bronze birds have similar bases.

The eyes are depressed circles at different levels in a triangular face. A fringe of hair is indicated by parallel vertical striations from the crown of the head to the nape of the neck. A flat belt crosses the back of the figure, and the stool on which he sits is divided into three horizontal rounded sections on the back only. The surface is

pitted in places, and some corrosion is present on chin and left shoulder and arm. The base, broken at the sitter's left, is hollow.

Cf. The closest parallel is the splendid little seated man on a circular base in the Louvre (MND 728). The underside of its base has hollow spaces between a circle in the middle and the four crescents tangent to it. The Pomerance man is also related to the seated or squatting figures on the terminals of the "bottle-stoppers" or pendants like No. 91 of this catalogue. Other figures sit atop hollow spheres (Metropolitan Museum 47.11.7, G. M. A. Richter, *Handbook of the Greek Collection* [Cambridge, Mass. 1953], pp. 22-23, pl. 13c). For larger figures seated on circular bases, an example in the Sparta Museum from the Sanctuary of Artemis Orthia is illustrated by R. Dawkins in *The Sanctuary of Artemis Arthia at Sparta* (London, 1929), pl. LXXVII a, and as newly cleaned by N. Himmelmann-Wildschütz. *Bemerkungen zur geometrischen Plastik* (Berlin, 1964), figs. 54-56. A comparable figure seated on a rectangular base is in the Walters Art Gallery, 54.789: D. K. Hill, *Catalogue of Classical Bronze Sculpture in the Walters Art Gallery* (Baltimore, 1949), p. 77, no. 167, pl. 36; N. Himmelmann-Wildschütz, *op. cit.*, figs. 51-53. (DGM)

90 Bird

Probably from Thessaly
Eighth to Early Seventh Century B.C.
Bronze with green patina
Height: 6.6 cm (2⅝ in.)

With its high rectangular comb balancing the flattened bladelike tail, this rooster or "peacock" was probably suspended by a loop on the center of the back, perhaps in an outdoor sanctuary. Its style is described as Geometric by art historians.

The legs are flat bars, joined at the bottom edge and incised in a simple zigzag pattern of five detached straight lines. There are small "spurs" below the center of the inside surfaces of the legs.

Three birds from Pherai in Thessaly are close parallels; now in the National Museum in Athens, and unpublished, they are numbers 15497, 1; 15497, 2 and 15497, 3. (DGM)

91 Geometric Bronze Object

Eighth to Seventh Century B.C.
Bronze
Height: 8.8 cm (3⁷⁄₁₆ in.)

A large number of these peculiar bronze objects have been found in northern Greece, from Thessaly to Macedonia. Their common feature is a rod from which project several rows of mushroom-shaped knobs. A squatting, apelike figure sits on top. Some of these objects are heavy and solid-cast, with a more recognizably naturalistic squatting figure; in others, the seated form disintegrates into a cut-out pattern.

Different functions have been proposed for these objects. U. Jantzen, in "Geometrische Kannenverschlüsse," *Archäologischer Anzeiger, Beiblatt zum Jahrbuch des Deutschen Archäologischen Instituts* 68 (1953), cols. 55-67, suggests that they may have been bottle stoppers, "Kannenverschlüsse," with the knobs wrapped by resin-soaked cords. C. Rolley, in *Collection Hélène Stathatos* III, *Objets antiques et byzantins* (Strasbourg, 1963), nos. 36-38, pp. 100, 242, pl. XIV, favors their use as pendants, a reasonable suggestion. (DGM)

92 Athena

Sixth Century B.C.
Bronze with dark gray-green patina
Height: 6.3 cm (2½ in.)

Athena, proud and forceful daughter of Zeus, strides in statues and vases brandishing a spear in her right hand, carrying a shield on her left forearm and helmeted with noble plumed crest. That this "Palladion" form begins early in the seventh century is shown by a statuette found at Olympia (E. Kunze, VII. *Olympiabericht*, pls. 70-71). Another now in the Bührle Collection, Zürich (R. Lullies, *Griechische Plastik, Vasen und Kleinkunst, Leihgaben aus Privatbesitz*, Staatliche Kunstsammlungen Kassel, 27 May-27 September 1964, no. 15) is dated in the first half of the sixth century. Still another sixth century Athena in this pose is the "Athena Mariemont," (E. Langlotz, *Frühgriechische Bildhauerschulen* [Nürnberg, 1927], p. 87, no. 30, pl. 47b; Mariemont, Collection Warocqué 31).

The bust is smoothed on the under side. Most unusual is the medallion over the forehead and the turban-like effect of what may be the hair under the helmet. (DGM)

Cf. the amphoras filled with oil and presented as prizes to victors in the Panathenaic games which had representations of Athena Palladion from the sixth century. One of many fine examples is the black-figure vase of the early fifth century B.C. attributed to the Kleophrades painter, Metropolitan Museum, 07.286.79, *CVA*, Metropolitan Museum of Art, New York, Fasc. 3, pl. 43, 1. Athena is depicted at the beginning of her career, at her birth, on the *skyphos* No. 111 of the Pomerance Collection. Mr. Pomerance has pointed to a similar bronze Athena from Delphi: J. Charbonneaux, *Greek Bronzes* (New York, 1962), p. 141, pl. VII 3.

93 Youth as a Patera Handle

Said to come from South Italy
End of the Sixth Century B.C.
Bronze
Height: 24.4 cm (9⁹⁄₁₆ in.)

A young man poised on a ram's head and crowned by two adorsed rams and simple volutes once served as a handle for a broad, saucer-like dish used for libations. Attributed to the Peloponnesus and South Italy by Gjødesen, this handle is of his type IIB.

The back of the figure is well-modeled, if simply, with fingers roughly indicated and hair textured with short, regular horizontal indentations. The palmette-shaped attachment is lightly incised on the reverse, but the volute and animal sections are plain.

BIBLIOGRAPHY: Queens College Catalogue, p. 21, no. 130; illus., p. 50; *Ancient Art*, p. 35, no. 135, pls. 44, 49, for full bibliography of studies of patera handles.
A nearly identical handle is in the Fogg Museum, 1960.481, in the David M. Robinson Collection. Another very similar piece appeared in *Auction Sale XIV*, Monnaies et Medailles S.A., Bâle, June 19, 1954, no. 24, pl. 8. The Royal Ontario Museum possesses an intact patera with handle which is also close to the Pomerance piece, T. A. Heinrich, *Art Treasures in the Royal Ontario Museum* (University of Toronto, 1963), p. 102-3, no. 957.161. Mogens Gjødesen, *Acta Archaeologica* XV, Fasc. 3, (1944) pp. 101-187 discusses several types of patera handles as do Amandry and Jantzen in more recent publications; see *Ancient Art* reference cited in Bibliography above.

94 Dancing Figure

Said to be from Alexandria
Second to First Century B.C.
Bronze with some green patina
Height: 10.0 cm (4¹⁵⁄₁₆ in.)

This figure is akin to the jar-carrying dwarf, No. 95. These boys and men, with sashes tied around their waists, may represent fishermen and are commonly associated with Alexandria, the Egyptian seaport of Hellenistic years. The head of this man is apparently bald except for a top-lock at the crown, and the eyes are inlaid in silver, with the pupils lost. The misshapen head and features were exploited in Hellenistic times for graphic, ofttimes brutal, descriptions of ethnic types and deformed outcasts. (DGM)

For other twisting, dancing figures which exist in bronze, see P. Perdrizet, *Bronzes grecs d'Egypte de la Collection Fouquet* (Paris, 1911), p. 65-67, no. 102, pls. XXIX, above right and left; XXX, XXXI, above and below. The author considers all of these figures to be involved in a violent dance accompanied by *crotala* or clappers of wood or ivory. A heavily veiled female dancer twists equally vigorously; she is the famous "Baker Dancer" and is illustrated in *Ancient Art*, p. 37, no. 144, pls. 44, 50, 51.

95 Statuette of a Dwarf

First Century B.C.
Bronze
Height: 8.1 cm (3 3/16 in.)

These caricatures or grotesques are widely spread in Hellenistic times, with Alexandria probably one of the centers. In his fundamental papers in the *Annual of the British School of Athens*, IX, 1902-1903, pp. 226-229; and in X, 1903-04, pp. 103-114, A. J. B. Wace has cited ancient evidence for the belief that phallic dwarfs and other grotesques were apotropaic. He thought that such bronzes were charms against the evil eye. They probably continued to be made in Roman times. (GMAH)

The figure is cast in one piece with the top flange of the base; the cylindrical part of the base is hollow and shows a black incrustation. A small hole, 0.15 cm in diameter, pierces the top of the elongated skull. The vase that the deformed creature carries may be a pointed alabastron. (For a more usual alabastron shape, see No. 109 and No. 110 of the Pomerance group.) It may, however, be a one-handled vase.

BIBLIOGRAPHY: Christie's *Catalogue*, 19-22 April 1920, no. 413, 1; *ex* Sir Guy Francis Laking. Christie's *Northwick Park Collection Catalogue* (Spencer-Churchill), 21 June 1965, p. 132, no. 514, pl. 72. Cf. D. Levi, *Antioch Mosaic Pavements* (Princeton, 1947), pl. 4 for dwarf with evil eye. A very similar piece is in H. C. Van Gulik, *Catalogue of Bronzes in the Allard Pierson Museum* (Amsterdam, 1940), pp. 9-10, no. 15, pl. XXX, the figure and pose almost identical to the Pomerance dwarf.

96 Fragment of a Helmet

Late Seventh to Mid-Sixth Century B.C.
Bronze
Height: 25 cm (9⅞ in.)

The so-called "Illyrian" helmets have been found in some numbers as dedications at Olympia and seem to have been favored in northern Greece as well as in the Peloponnesus, to judge from the finds in burials of the sixth century B.C. in the former region. In some cases the helmets discovered in burials have been accompanied by masks of gold foil—for example, the Illyrian helmet and gold mask group recently acquired by the Walters Art Gallery, Baltimore. The class to which the Pomerance helmet belongs, the "ripe Illyrian helmet," is dated in the late seventh to the middle of the sixth century B.C.

For the Baltimore pieces, see *Archaeology* 18, 1 (1965), p. 64. Compare E. Kunze, "Helme," *VI. Bericht über die Ausgrabungen in Olympia* (Berlin, 1958), pp. 137-138. Close parallels, with two ridges across the forehead and knobbed rivets bordering the edges of the cheekpieces and the opening for the face are illustrated in pls. 46-49. (DGM)
See also B. Filow, *Die archaische Nekropole von Trebenischte* (Berlin and Leipzig, 1927), p. 8, fig. 7, nos. 1, 2; pl. I, 2 (mask); pl. XV, 2 (helmet).

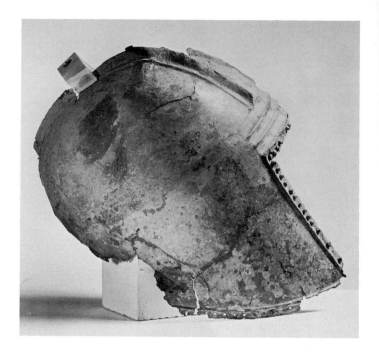

97 Corinthian Helmet and Greaves

Said to have been found in Sicily
Fifth Century B.C.
Bronze
Height of helmet: 30.5 cm (12 in.)
Height of each greave: 39 cm (15⁹⁄₁₆ in.)

Helmets and greaves were part of the essential protection of the Greek warrior for generations. In addition, he carried a shield and spear, and sometimes a short sword; a cuirass, or chest protector, as well as arm and upper leg guards were also included in a full armor. Warriors arming were a popular subject for vase decoration; in this collection, it is represented on the *skyphos*, No. 111, and the amphora, No. 112.

BIBLIOGRAPHY: University of Pennsylvania Catalogue, no. 9.
Cf. an armor group in the Museum of Fine Arts, Boston, dated to the late sixth century B.C., which includes a Corinthian helmet and a single greave of simpler form: C. C. Vermeule III, *The Classical Journal* 57, 4 (1962), pp. 145-147, fig. 1, notes 2-4. (DGM) A helmet bearing a similar design of confronting snakes was seen by Mr. Pomerance in the German Excavation House at Olympia in 1964, and is probably that published by E. Kunze in *Deltion* 17 (1961-62), "Chronika," p. 117, pl. 132. In the Cassel Museum, Germany is a set of helmet and greaves of the same type as this armor: Inv. Br 703.1 and 703.2 soon to be published by R. Lullies in *Archäologischer Anzeiger*, 1966. Erich Kukahn has made a study of the history and formal development of the Greek helmet, and particularly the Corinthian style, in his dissertation, "Der griechische Helm" (Marburg, 1936), including a catalogue of 167 examples.

98 Horse

Attic
Late Eighth Century B.C.
Terracotta with black
Height: 11.6 cm (4⁹⁄₁₆ in.)

This little horse is said to have had three companions and probably decorated the lid of a large vase, probably a pyxis. Mr. von Bothmer suggests that, since the head is turned slightly to right, the horse may have been the right-hand or trace horse of the quadriga group.

The horse's head is repaired and a surface incrustation covers the tail, inside the hindlegs and the underbelly. There is some wear, particularly the glaze around the neck and left leg. Traces of glue or resin are visible on the neck.

Cf. examples of similar horses and groups of chariot horses cited in *Kerameikos: Ergebnisse der Ausgrabungen* (Berlin) 5, pt. 1 (1954), p. 121; additional examples in R. S. Young, "Late Geometric Graves and a Seventh Century Well in the [Athenian] Agora," *Hesperia Supplement* II (1939), pp. 80, 83, no. XVII 15, figs. 54-55; pp. 80, 84-5, no. XVII 17, figs. 54, 56; pp. 89, 90, 91-92, no. XVIII 6, figs. 60-61, etc. all *trigae* or three-horse groups. Pyxides in various sizes and materials served a variety of purposes; see No. 77 for a small stone vessel. They were also box- or basket-shaped.

99 Seated Goddess

Archaic Greek
Sixth Century B.C.
Buff terracotta with red and yellow paint
Height: 18.0 cm (7⅛ in.)

Terracotta figurines were manufactured in the Archaic Period for deposit in graves and as inexpensive offerings dedicated in temples. They took a variety of forms; compare the rooster, No. 102, and the pomegranate, No. 103, and the later so-called Tanagra type, No. 105. From the magnificence of her headdress and the solemnity of her pose, we assume that this lady is a goddess.

Details of garment and crown are painted predominantly in red; golden yellow appears in the centers of the large discs on the head and some stripes on the garment. The lady leans slightly backward resting on a rough columnar support (restored) that joins the figure below waist level in back. The top of the crown, neck, the right arm and the skirt below the "knees" have been reattached.

BIBLIOGRAPHY: University of Pennsylvania Catalogue, no. 12.
Cf. a similar though larger and less well preserved seated goddess in the Museum of Fine Arts, Boston (18.45).

100   Horse and Rider

Possibly Boeotian
Sixth or Fifth Century B.C.
Pale brown terracotta with traces of white, red and black
  paint
Height: 14.0 cm (5½ in.)

These small, charming "sketches" in terracotta were
manufactured by the hundreds in many parts of Greece as
votive offerings for sanctuaries. The horse, with hand-
modeled and pinched features, has light zigzag lines run-
ning down its mane, visible against a dark ground. The
diminutive rider does not clasp his steed's neck as is common, but seems firmly to grasp imaginary reins. (DGM)

The man's head is bird-like; his right arm is broken
away. On the right haunch of the horse is a dot rosette
with a red center and white outer dots. The animal's tail
is repaired at the base; also mended is the left leg of the
rider. There is a small hole in each of the horse's
shoulders. The figure is apparently solid.

Cf. numerous examples of this type illustrated in A. N. Stillwell,
Corinth, XV, 2, "The Potters' Quarter, the Terracottas" (Princeton,
1952), pls. 35 ff. In general the modeling is less sophisticated, but
features are sometimes painted; the horses' manes are often higher
between the ears than on the Pomerance piece.

101   Horse with Woman Riding Sidesaddle

Fifth Century B.C.
Coarse pinkish terracotta, with traces of paint
Height: 13.8 cm (5⁷⁄₁₆ in.)

Unusual here is the combination of a small mold-made
female figurine with a handmade horse. This combination
of subjects goes back, however, at least as far as Mycenaean times, and reappears in two Geometric bronzes.
The conservatively archaic style of the cloaked woman
makes the first half of the fifth century B.C. a likely date.

The hind legs of the horse have been repaired at knee
level, and the tail has been reattached at the base. A grey
incrustation covers most of the statuette, with areas of
white on top of it.

One of the bronzes which comes from Olympia: E. Kunze, "Bronze-
statuetten," *IV. Bericht über die Ausgrabungen in Olympia* (Berlin,
1940-41), pl. 107, inv. no. B 1750, pl. 33, 1. The second example —
from Lusoi — is now in the Kunsthistorisches Museum, Vienna
(2904): Kunze, *op. cit.*, p. 107, fig. 89. Doro Levi cites a terracotta
figurine of the Mycenaean period in Chapter III, "Mobilier funéraire
de Kharvati (Attique)," *Collection Hélène Stathatos*, II, *Les Objets
antiques et byzantins* (Strasbourg, 1963), pp. 23-24, no. 6, pl. II, and
fig. 10. A discussion of archaic terracottas appears in Kunze, *op. cit.*,
p. 107, note 2. (DGM)

102 Rooster

Early Fifth Century B.C.
Terracotta with traces of red paint on lower wing and
 yellow on neck
Height: 18 cm (7¹/₁₆ in.)

Such votive offerings, popular in the fifth and fourth
centuries, recall Socrates' last request in the *Phaedo:*
"Give a cock for me to Asklepios." The birds usually
rest, as here, on tail and abbreviated feet which form a
low tripod support. (DGM) Clay cocks as well as other
animal figurines have also been found in burial deposits.

Probably formed in a two-part mold, the bird is hollow
and has a small irregular hole on the underside.

Cf. Higgins, *Terracottas,* I, nos. 187 and particularly 188, both
excavated at Camiros on Rhodes. The modeling and shape of the
pieces are similar, with the exception of the shape of the comb, which
diminishes in height toward the beak on the Rhodian birds. For an
earlier, smaller version of a rooster in bronze probably also used as
a votive offering, see No. 90 of this catalogue. A Rhodian aryballos
(in the form of a rooster) of the late sixth century is in the Metropolitan Museum (41.162.199): *CVA,* U.S.A. Fasc. I, p. 19, no. 8, pl.
30, 8.

103 Pomegranate

Mid-Fifth Century B.C.
Buff-colored terracotta with traces of blue and white
 paint
Height: 7.1 cm (2¹³/₁₆ in.)

Like the preceding cock, this fruit was a votive offering
perhaps connected with the mysteries of the Eleusinian
cult or with local worship of underworld gods. It is frequently held in the hands by maidens who serve as
handles or supports for standing mirrors. In small
figures such as the bronze No. 125, the pomegranate may
be held in one hand and a dove in the other. Terracotta
figures of the late sixth and early fifth centuries holding
these two attributes against their bodies have been found
in the Potters' Quarter of Corinth.

The small hole in the top of the fruit is a vent hole.
Upper and lower molds were probably used to form the
object.

Cf. Higgins, *op. cit.,* nos. 201, 203, and particularly 198, all of which
come from Camiros, Rhodes. A mirror support in the form of a
maiden carrying pomegranate and dove is illustrated in J. Charbonneaux, *Les Bronzes grecs* (Paris, 1958), pl. IV, 1; the bronze is in
the National Museum, Athens. For the terracotta figures from Corinth,
see A. N. Stillwell, *Corinth* XV, part II (Princeton, 1952), p. 15, X,
19; X, 24).

104 Statuette of Young Girl

Fifth to Fourth Century B.C.
Pinkish terracotta with traces of color
Height: 14.7 cm (5¹³⁄₁₆ in.)

Similar figurines are known both from Tanagra and from Myrina in Asia Minor. The plump figure and round face of this little girl are evidence of an awakening interest of Greek artists in the personalities, moods and actual appearance of children. A group of marble statuettes of the late fifth century has been found recently at the sanctuary of Artemis at Brauron; these are the *arktoi*—"bears" —or girl priestesses. (DGM) Children also appeared on grave stelae of the fifth to fourth century in natural poses with prized possessions such as pets, as on the stelae of a little girl with doves from Paros and an older girl with pomegranate from Boeotia in New York.

The hair of the figure is arranged in what has been called the "melon coiffure" and has been textured with short indentations, probably after molding. A roundish vent hole, about 1.3 cm in diameter, opens in the back at waist level. The statuette was apparently formed in a two-part mold; the flat base may have been added separately. Traces of dark red remain on the hair, and two shades of blue on the chiton. The folded mantle crosses the back below the waist and is wrapped over the girl's left wrist.

The two stelae are in the Metropolitan Museum of Art, 27.45 and 11.141 respectively.

105 Woman in a Mantle

Late Fourth or Third Century B.C.
Pale orange-pink terracotta with traces of white paint or
   slip
Height: 24.5 cm (9⅝ in.)

During the fourth century, thousands of small terracotta figures, mostly female, were made as offerings for the dead. They were molded in a variety of poses and compositions, and often vividly painted. Two major centers emerge as sources for these statuettes—Myrina in Asia Minor and Tanagra in Boeotia on the Greek mainland. From the latter comes the name often used to designate the object type. This pose, the woman enveloped in a heavy mantle which reveals only the lower part of the chiton worn beneath, has been called the "Sophoclean" type, in reference to stone statues of the philosopher dressed in a similar fashion.

The fabric of the figurine is about 0.5 cm thick, with small areas of black discoloration at bottom of skirt and back of mantle. Between the upper arms in back is an irregularly square vent hole. Most of the undergarment has been broken away. The remaining portion of the figure has been neatly repaired from four large fragments. At the crown of the head, on top of the "folded napkin," is a small wad of clay, possibly a broken attachment for a hat.

BIBLIOGRAPHY: *Auktion II Antike Kunstwerke 14. May 1960*, Ars Antiqua AG, Luzern, p. 33, no. 75, pl. 35:75.
Cf. a brief commentary on "Tanagra figures" made in Museum of Fine Arts, *Greek, Etruscan and Roman Art* (Boston, 1963), pp. 142-144. The subject is more fully considered by G. Kleiner, *Tanagrafiguren, Untersuchungen zur hellenistischen Kunst und Geschichte* (Berlin, 1942). Here, the "Sophoclean" type is discussed, pp. 95 ff. For a large stone statue of Sophocles, see K. Schefold, *Die Bildnisse der antiken Dichter, Redner und Denker* (Basel, 1943) p. 93. Kleiner illustrates Berlin no. 6312, *op. cit.*, pl. 5a, a figure in pose and drapery arrangement very like the Pomerance figurine except that the head is turned more to the right and covered with a blousy cap. The folded napkin-like head covering appears in a Myrina piece now in Istanbul, no. M 2521, Kleiner's pl. 17a. To observe the wide gamut of style in female terracotta figurines, recall No. 99, the "Seated Goddess" of the sixth century.

106 An Arimasp Fighting a Griffin

Tarantine
Third Quarter of Fourth Century B.C.
Terracotta with gilding
Height: 6.5 cm (2⁹⁄₁₆ in.)   Length: 15.2 cm (6 in.)

His short chiton, leggings, pelta-shaped shield and Phrygian cap indicate the Eastern connections of this warrior
of the legendary one-eyed Scythian tribe known as Arimasps. They battled the griffins, marvelous part-lion, part-
eagle creatures, who guarded the mines and gold of the
Hyperboreans, a mythological people who lived beyond
the north wind in eternal sunshine and abundance. The
struggle depicted here is one of several small molded
reliefs which were probably applied to a wooden sar-

cophagus. The two figures are disconnected by a break in the griffin's front right paw.

BIBLIOGRAPHY: R. Lullies, *Vergoldete Terrakotta-Appliken aus Tarent* VII (Heidelberg, 1962), p. 10, no. 2 and p. 78, pl. 2,2. The monograph considers in detail the type, with numerous examples, remarks on technique, dating, meaning, etc. *Auction XIV, June 19, 1954, Classical Antiquities,* Monnaies et Medailles S.A., no. 15, A (one of two in the lot), pl. 4.
K. Schefold, *Meisterwerke griechischer Kunst* (Basel and Stuttgart, 1960), pp. 266-267, no. VII 354 gives an idea of the variety of subjects used for these appliqués. On pp. 93-94, Schefold compares the wooden sarcophagi with wooden reliefs from Alexandria and South Russia and proposes that the Arimasps were servants of Dionysos and that their battle with the griffins is symbolic of the way from death to immortality. A griffin closely parallel with this griffin is in the Metropolitan Museum (20.223): Lullies, *op. cit.,* p. 18, 1; pl. 15, 2.

107   Torso of a Youth

Possibly from Egypt
Late Sixth Century B.C.
Plaster
Height: 23.4 cm (9¼ in.)

At least by the seventh century B.C. the Greeks in Egypt had settled in a town called Naucratis in the western part of the present Delta. According to Herodotus, the town was famous in the ancient world for its sanctuaries to Greek gods and its pivotal position in foreign trade to Egypt. This ancient plaster cast of a torso reflects the connection between the Archaic Greek *kouros* and the standing statue long traditional in Egypt. The hands clenched and hugging the hips, the left leg forward, the rest of the body strictly frontal—all of these characteristics can be seen in Egyptian figures since the Old Kingdom. What appears to be rather more Greek is the figure's nudity.

A light yellowish color covers the front and sides of the model. A long break down the near center and another across the hips have been very neatly repaired.

BIBLIOGRAPHY: *Auktion II, Antike Kunstwerke, 14 May 1960,* Ars Antiqua AG Luzern, p. 15, no. 26, pl. 12.
C. G. Edgar lists a small alabaster torso, 27426, that closely parallels this cast: *Greek Sculpture - Catalogue général des antiquités égyptiennes du Musée du Caire* (Cairo, 1903), pp. 1 f., pl. I. He notes, p. 1, that such stone figures possibly were not intended to be presented naked; some of them do have traces of paint probably intended to represent garments. A limestone example is included by W. M. Flinders-Petrie, *Naukratis* I (London, 1886), pl. 1, no. 4. It has been suggested that the Pomerance piece is a sculptor's model. Parallels have been drawn to Greek *kouroi*; see Ars Antiqua Catalogue entry cited above for additional comparative bibliography.

108 Antefix in the Form of a Human Head

Said to be from Sicily
Possibly Fifth to Fourth Century B.C.
Pinkish terracotta, with inclusions
Height: 28.5 cm (11¼ in.)

An architectural element used to mask the gutter ends of roofing tiles, this antefix may represent a female head.

It is heavy ware, and traces of a yellow-white substance are found in the depressions of the features and hair. The back appears to have been flattened in modern times.

The Etruscan antefix, No. 135, represents a female head, perhaps a maenad or female follower of Dionysos. DGM suggests that this Sicilian piece may be part of a standing *protome* on a bench, such as have been found in Morgantina.

109 Alabastron with Two Lions

Corinthian
Seventh or Sixth Century B.C.
Buff terracotta with black and red color
Height: 8.3 cm (3¼ in.)

Tiny vessels like this black-figure alabastron and the one that follows, No. 110, were used for perfumes, oils and small amounts of precious liquids. Corinth, at the isthmus connecting the Peloponnesus, became a major pottery center of the ancient world during the seventh and sixth centuries. Characteristic are the buff-colored ware and the black and red glazed decoration of exotic animals apparently of Eastern origin, in the style called "Orientalizing." The heraldic lions with curving, intertwined tails and the space fillers, rosettes and petal-shaped forms appear on vases of all sizes and shapes in this period. See our No. 110.

A small pierced handle appears to have been pinched under the lip of the wheel-made body. There are radiating bands on the top of the lip; glazed colors vary somewhat as a result of firing. The surface is scratched in places and has some black discoloration.

Cf. a Corinthian alabastron in the Metropolitan Museum of Art (30.115.26) decorated with two lions face to face and circular rosettes with crossed incised lines to indicate petals as on the Pomerance piece.

110 Alabastron with Lion, Panther and Goose

Corinthian
Sixth Century B.C.
Buff terracotta with red and black color
Height: 8.9 cm (3½ in.)

This small vase, like No. 109, is decorated in the "Orientalizing" style, with a lion and a panther (the latter species, as always, depicted with body in profile and head full-face). Another alabastron with the same asymmetrical grouping of animals, attributed to the Antithetical Painter by Amyx, is in the Pavlos Kanellopoulos Collection in Athens.

Part of the lip is broken away and the color is worn off the hind quarters of the animals. The incisions used to emphasize details are less careful than on the preceding object. Dots decorate the round bottom rather than the radiating petal forms that embellish No. 109.

111 Skyphos

Attic
About 540-530 B.C.
Buff terracotta with black, white and red color
Height: 12 cm (4¾ in.)

Such a drinking cup would hold a generous draught of wine, even if it were mixed with water as was probably the case. The black-figure decoration shows on the obverse, as in a formal tableau, the birth of Athena. While her usual attributes, helmet and armor, are not present, she stands before her father Zeus, full-grown as she has sprung from his head. On the reverse, a warrior prepares to depart for battle, putting on his second greave as the rest of his equipment waits, some in the hands of solemn spectators.

In the Pomerance Collection, there are several vessels traditionally devoted to wine—in addition to the *skyphos*, the *stamnos* (No. 113), the *rhyton* (No. 116) and the *olpe* (No. 137). For armor that protected a warrior of a later date than the man represented here, see No. 96 and No. 97, a,b,c. Still another warrior arms himself on No. 112.

Dietrich von Bothmer has attributed this vase to the Painter of the Nicosia Olpe and cites another skyphos by the same hand in the collection of Norman Davis, Seattle. Both of these *skyphoi*, as well as a third (Athens, 363), include the same combination of scenes. In the Seattle and Athens vases, three figures are grouped on each side of the central person, and a siren reposes under each handle. Beazley lists the vases attributed to the Nicosia Olpe Painter in *Attic Black-figure Vase-painters* (Oxford, 1956), pp. 452-453, 698.

112 Amphora

Attic
About 540-530 B.C.
Red terracotta with black, red and white color
Height: 48.4 cm (19¹⁄₁₆ in.)

In shape this is one of several variations on the two-handled vase called amphora. One of the pictures represents the gods Athena and Ares fighting giants in a version of the mythological *gigantomachy* or battle between the Olympian gods and the earthly giants. The reverse panel shows a man preparing for combat, closely attended by two older men and two youths. The top edge of each panel is decorated by a palmette-lotus border. Beazley attributes this amphora to the Swing Painter.

BIBLIOGRAPHY: J. D. Beazley, *Attic Black-figure Vase-painters* (Oxford, 1956), p. 693, no. 34 bis (addendum to pp. 304-310); *Ancient Art*, p. 52, no. 109, pls. 74, 75.

113 Stamnos

Attic
About 480 B.C.
Terracotta with black color
Height: 29 cm (11½ in.)

This wide-mouthed jar was used for wine or water. One of the figures represented in the simple but dramatic decorative scheme is Poseidon, wielding his traditional trident and carrying a dolphin, one of the creatures of his sea domain. He is pursuing Aethra, who glances back over her shoulder as if to measure the distance between them and carries a wool basket in the hand free from the heavy mantle. Aethra was daughter of Pittheus (a ruler of Troezen in the Peloponnesus), beloved of immortal Poseidon and mother of Theseus, one of the greatest of the legendary Greek hero-kings. This red-figure painting style has been attributed by Beazley to the Hephaisteion Painter.

The surface is somewhat scratched on the outside; the inside is not glazed below the neck. The glaze has fired to reddish and greenish black on the shoulder of the vase and in some other areas.

BIBLIOGRAPHY: Queens College Catalogue, p. 23, no. 169, ill. p. 59; J. D. Beazley, *Attic Red-figure Vase-painters* (Oxford, 1963), second edition, vol. I, p. 298, no. 3.
Cf. a similar use of two large figures related to each other by tradition one on each side of a vase; London E439, from Vulci, with Dionysos brandishing a slain fawn and a satyr playing a flute, in *CVA*, British Museum Fasc. 3, III I c may be by the same painter. The palmettes at the handles and the tongue pattern around the lip of the vase are almost identical to those of the present piece, as has been pointed out by Beazley.

114 Bell-krater

Italiote
Late Fifth Century B.C.
Pale orange-red terracotta with black color
Height: 33.7 cm (13¼ in.)

On this large vessel used for mixing wine and water, a rather sedate maenad advances a thyrsos toward a nude silen on the right who is carrying a horn. Between the two figures usually involved in Dionysiac revels, a satyr herm confronts the spectator. On the reverse, three mantled youths stand as if in quiet conversation. A. D. Trendall attributes the vase to the Cyclops Painter, an off-shoot of the Pisticci Painter but of the same workshop.

The fabric of the vase seems to become nearly white toward the lip. There is some crackling of the glaze on the inside of the handles and parts of the interior of the vase. There is some repainting in the red-figure decoration.

BIBLIOGRAPHY: Sale Catalogue (Luzern), *Galerie Fischer*, 21 June 1955, no. 79, pl. 6; A. D. Trendall, "Il Pittore del Ciclope," *Atti e Memorie della Società Magna Grecia* (Rome, 1960), New Series III, pp. 85-92, pls. XX-XXIII; this vase, p. 86, no. 12, pl. XXI, c,d. Also letter from Trendall dated 19 November 1956, where he comments that ". . . full-face herms are uncommon . . ."
Of the Cyclops Painter vases listed by Trendall, the vase most similar to the Pomerance krater would seem to be his no. 13, Vienna 924 (SK 216,64), of like height and with the same combination of figures on both the obverse and the reverse. The youth with the mantle pulled up over his head appears to be out of the usual pattern for the painter. The head of a traditional and more serious type of herm is No. 86 of this Catalogue.

115 Lekythos with Mourners at a Tomb

Attic
Late Fifth Century B.C.
Terracotta with black, orange and white color
Height: 34 cm. (13⅜ in.)

The *lekythos* is an oil flask or perfume bottle which was used as a toilet article as well as for offerings to the dead. It had taken this particular shape by the beginning of the fifth century B.C. with the tomb motif used for decoration almost exclusively by the middle of that century. This particular *lekythos* can be attributed to the Reed Painter who was associated by his loose, sketchy painting style to several *lekythos* painters referred to as the "R Group."

The black glaze is worn at the lip and the base; the white slip seems to be abraded behind the female figure and below the handle. There is an altar-like structure behind the stele which is draped with three fillets. The free, almost hasty style is exemplified by the overlapping of the stele on the meander band; however, the drawing in the figure of the youth particularly is limpid and expressive.

Cf. J. D. Beazley, *Attic Red-figure Vase-painters* 2nd edition, vol. II, pp. 1376-1382, 1692, for the Reed Painter's works.

116 Deer-head Rhyton

Said to come from Turkey, near ancient Smyrna
Fourth Century B.C.
Terracotta with black and white decoration
Height: 19.9 cm. (7¹³⁄₁₆ in.)

A drinking cup with one handle and the lower part formed into a human or, more frequently, an animal head, the *rhyton's* name describes in Greek how it functioned; the liquid flowed into the mouth from a hole in the end of the vessel.

The left horn of the deer and part of this cup's rim are broken away. The interior is glazed black. Joints of the parts of the head mould and of the cup and head at the base of the ears are apparent on the inside. The handle is concave in section. The muzzle of this red-figured vessel is pierced; the vessel was probably used as a beaker.

H. Hoffmann has collected several animal *rhyta* in his *Attic Red-figured Rhyta* (Mainz, 1962). He extends his discussion begun in *Antike Kunst* 4 (1961),1, pp. 21-26, pls. 8-12. The article which pertains most directly to the present piece is his "Two Deer Heads from Apulia," *AJA* 64 (1960), pp. 276-278, pls. 77-78. Here Hoffmann describes the manner in which *rhyta* were made and refers to the possible patrix of a mould for deer-head cups in the Metropolitan Museum, 10.210.124. The Metropolitan deer *rhyton* is glazed black, but similar in shape to the Pomerance deerhead. See also J. V. Noble, *The Technique of Painted Attic Pottery* (New York, 1965), pp. 22 and 28-30. It has been suggested that "imitative reproductions" of Ionian deer appear in the Treasure of Panagurishte. Several gold vessels including three deer-head bent *rhyta* of the fourth century B.C. are illustrated in D. Zontschew, *Der Goldschatz von Panagjurischte* (Berlin, 1959).

117 Askos with Scylla

Probably from Canosa
Early Third Century B.C.
Buff-colored terracotta with traces of color
Height: 36.3 cm (14$\frac{5}{16}$ in.)

Scylla and her neighbor the whirlpool Charybdis were the destruction of many Greek sailors in mythological times, including some hapless men of Odysseus' crew. One of the several versions of the monster's appearance is represented here—the womanly torso surmounting a sea-serpent body with three hounds issuing from her hips. The crest, or wave, pattern is used here, not purely decoratively as is frequent in Classical ornament, but actually related to sea creatures and events. Although the pottery *askos* was derived from an animal-skin vessel, large decorated vases of this type were part of the furniture of the tomb and apparently were not actually used to hold liquid.

The main body of the vessel seems to have been moulded. The plastic crest, the dolphins and Scylla were made separately and attached; the mouth and neck were wheel-made. Dolphins and crest were probably also moulded. Other marine creatures, many less fanciful, emerge in the traces of color that cover much of the vase; below the modeled crest, front and back, yellow areas with black spots resemble octopi which move among circular rosettes painted in black line. The same colors depict flat-bodied fish with red fins swimming above the waves among the dolphins but in the opposite direction. On the crest, the dolphins, the dogs, and the body of Scylla below the waist are traces of blue paint. Above the dolphins appear very indistinct vestiges of a painted crest composed of palmettes and floral forms. Red color remains on Scylla's helmet, lips, the upper painted crest and elsewhere. All of the color seems to have been applied over white. The bottom has been restored; the arms of the she-monster and the left leg of the central dog have been repaired; the body has a few hairline cracks and areas of beige incrustation.

Cf. nearly a dozen of these highly decorated vases which have been collected by Andrew Oliver, Jr. and will appear in a forthcoming article on two Canosan tombs. Mr. Oliver notes that most are apparently Canosan in origin and of the third century B.C. A vividly painted example reposes in Boston, Museum of Fine Arts, 99.541. Plastic elements also appear on Louvre Cp3811 and Karlsruhe B656 (*CVA* Karlsruhe, pl. 86 for the latter). The trapezoidal shape of the Pomerance *askos* is found on British Museum D203 (*CVA* British Museum Fasc. VII, IV Da, 17, 3). The Metropolitan Museum's red-figure example is less complete and numbered 96.18.58.

ETRUSCAN ART

Compiled by Jean L. Keith
Contributors, G.M.A. Hanfmann and
David G. Mitten

118   Horse Bit

Villanovan
Ninth to Eighth Century B.C.
Bronze
Height: 16 cm (6⁵⁄₁₆ in.)
Width from loop to loop of snaffle, including pendants:
      19 cm (7½ in.)

The Iron Age predecessors of the Etruscans in Italy must have been owners of handsomely equipped horses. Bits of bronze and iron, and ornamented harness parts have been found repeatedly in burials, in combination with tools and other living and ritual paraphernalia. This bit, except for its elaborate decoration, is much like a modern snaffle. Horses and birds are incorporated into the cheekpiece, and pendants dangled in pairs from fore and hind "feet" of the dominating horse.

Cheekpieces formed of single horses attached to a bar for connection with the reins are not uncommon; see D. Randall-MacIver, *Villanovans and Early Etruscans* (Oxford, 1924), pl. 4, no. 1 and pl. 26, no. 7; both of these evidently had pendants hanging from "feet" front and back. Less complicated in design, but closer to this piece, is the bit in the Norbert Schimmel Collection (H. Hoffman, *Norbert Schimmel Collection*, no. 39). Additional bibliography can be found in H. Cahn, *Auktion XXII der Münzen und Medaillen* A.G. Basel, 13 May 1961, p. 36, no. 65, pl. 20:65. Pendants vary in shape but are generally symmetrical, sometimes including birds in the often pierced and elaborate compositions. A bronze cheekpiece with a "colt" on a horse and ducks between the legs was exhibited in *American Art in Private Collections* (Cambridge, Mass., 1954), p. 42, no. 367, pl. XCVII, and dated about 700 B.C. A rider and horse with a bird between its legs have been used to terminate each of the six legs of a bronze cauldron in the Metropolitan Museum of Art, 54.11.1.

119 Decorative Shield with Ram's Head Boss

Sixth Century B.C.
Bronze
Diameter: 28 cm (11 in.)

Neither the size nor the construction for use in battle,
this shield may have been used to decorate the panelled
ceiling of a tomb chamber, or burial furniture, such as a
sarcophagus or a funeral bed.

The eyes of the ram are inlaid in a sort of granular
white paste. There are areas of restoration on the shield.

A number of beaten bronze shield bosses in the shape of ram's
heads are known; for example, in the Museum of Fine Arts, Boston,
no. 08.534, and in the Rhode Island School of Design, no. 22.206.
In each case, the face is framed by enormous curling horns as in the
present piece. H. Jucker in *Kunst und Leben der Etrusker* (Ausstel-
lungskatalog Köln, 1956), p. 115, nos. 277-278, indicates that these
shields seem to be a specialty of Tarquinia and suggests a date of
the last quarter of the fourth century. (GMAH) Bosses were also
designed with heads of satyrs, lions, the river god Acheloos and other
subjects. See Giglioli, *L'arte etrusca*, pl. XCVII, 1 and 2, now in the
Museo Gregoriano, Vatican.

120   Statuette of a Discobolus

Second Quarter of the Fifth Century B.C.
Bronze
Height: 15.6 cm (6⅛ in.)

The little discus thrower served as a finial for a large candelabrum, or as a utensil used for the suspension of other tools such as ladles. The twist of the body, the glance of the head to the right suggest that the moment when the athlete appraises the cast of the discus is represented here.

The face is modeled in careful detail. The figure is cast in one piece with the connecting ring. The base is depressed inside, to the lowest level of the splay moulding.

BIBLIOGRAPHY: *Ancient Art.* p. 40, no. 154, pl. 54; includes reference to other implements used for suspension.

121   Youth

Not Later than Fifth Century B.C.
Bronze
Height: 13 cm (5⅛ in.)

The nude young man stands as if ready for wrestling, his left foot slightly advanced in the traditional stance of the *kouros*, a Greek form that developed from Egyptian standing statues. His broad shoulders and wide hips contrast with a narrow waist and almost feminine chest. The ears are simply modeled in a C-shape, and his back hair falls in a broad flap which is incised in vertical parallel lines and curls under at the lower edge. The rounded, slender physique recalls Ionian prototypes.

122   Incense Burner with Silen

Fifth Century B.C.
Bronze
Height: 31.8 cm (12⅛ in.)

A candelabrum, or more likely a *thymiaterion* (incense
burner), is supported by a silen. The base is a circular
stand resting on three winged lion paws. The silen,
with left foot forward and left hand raised as if pouring,
may well be dancing. In his right hand is the remnant of
a curved handle-like object. He has carefully incised hair,
wide shelving beard and the long, slender moustaches of
silens of the first half of the fifth century B.C. The
transition to the upright shaft of the candelabrum is made
by a faceted bronze bead form. The lower of the two
horizontal discs that divide the shaft into three equal
parts is incised with six concentric circles, as is the base
which also has an irregular incised tongue pattern. This
type of *thymiaterion* is known from the fifth century in
Central Etruria.

Cf. P. Ducati, *Storia dell'arte etrusca* (Firenze, 1927), pl. 117, fig.
310. (DGM) See Giglioli, *L'arte etrusca*, pl. CCX, 3, for similar
mouldings and discs. The combination of circular base and winged
feet attached separately is quite unusual in this type of object.

123   Satyr

Found at Bertoli, near Cortona
Said to be Fifth Century B.C.
Bronze
Height: 6.8 cm $(2^{11}\!/_{16}$ in.)

Dr. Herbert Cahn states that this little figure was found at Bertoli, near Cortona, in 1870, with a red-figure plate attributed to the Cerberus Painter. The plate is now in a private collection in Basle and is decorated with two dancing youths.

The beard of this bronze is textured with rows of short vertical indentations. The back hair is rendered in schematized wedge-shaped sections, with a row of small "curls" across the nape of the neck below a distinct dividing line. Some rust color is mixed with the pale to dark blue-green patina.

I know of no parallels for this figure in size and modeling of the torso. Its function is unclear, since there seem to be no pins for attachment on the underside of the circular base. The pose is common for figures of athletes, but another such satyr is not now known.

124   Warrior

Bronze
Height, including tenons: 19.1 cm $(7\!/_2$ in.)

The stocky soldier strides forward in a stance traditional among representations of Etruscan figures of fighters. His large-crested helmet is also typical.

The metal is blackened, with patches of green patina and some areas of pitting.

BIBLIOGRAPHY: Sale Catalogue (London), *Sotheby*, 5 March 1962, p. 53, no. 166 (ill.).
Mrs. E. Richardson believes this to be a good example of a popular type, dating from the first half of the fifth century B.C.

126 Mirror

Probably from Praeneste
Late Fourth Century B.C.
Bronze
Height: 31.6 cm (12⁷⁄₁₆ in.)

Some of the finest Etruscan engraving on bronze is found not only on *cistae* but also on mirrors. The designs and scenes often reveal a high degree of drawing and technical skill as well as mythological motifs of Greek origin. The sources seem to be Greek vase paintings rather than Greek mirrors, however. Handles cast in one piece with the mirror disc, as on the Pomerance piece, seem to come primarily from Praeneste, which also produced fewer mirrors with inscriptions and then, more likely in Latin than Etruscan.

This mirror is not inscribed and thus gives no clue to the identity of the figures represented; one nude woman, left center, two young men on either side of her, and a little boy at the right with a curious top knot. Dr. Kyle M. Phillips, Jr. suggests the fourth century date based on the mirror's shape and the "nervous quality" of the engraving. A palmette is engraved on the back of the mirror at the base of the handle. The handle tang itself terminates in an animal head, possibly cervine.

The leafed branch motif appears as a border with variations (double-lined stem, berries, etc.) on many Etruscan bronze objects. The plant form used to fill the space below the ground line on which the figures stand is less common but does appear with some differences on the bottom border of a *cista* in the Museum of Fine Arts, Boston (93.1439). Still closer, and in the same position on a mirror, is the flower motif found in E. Gerhard, A. Klügemann, G. Körte, *Etruskische Spiegel* (Berlin, 1840-1897), pl. XXVI, no. 27. A general article which discusses Etruscan mirrors is that by J. D. Beazley, "The World of the Etruscan Mirror," *Journal of Hellenic Studies* 69 (1949), pp. 1-17. The Gerhard work cited above remains the basic corpus of Etruscan mirrors, however.

125 Goddess or Worshiper

Second Half of the Fifth or Early Fourth Century B.C.
Bronze
Height: 8.9 cm (3½ in.)

Some scholars believe the type represents Turan, Etruscan goddess of love, others, worshiping women. Created before the middle of the fifth century, as is the fine large bronze of the Fogg Museum (1956.43), the type continued to be made in smaller examples well into the fourth century B.C. (GMAH)

The body of the lady is very thin, and the back of the torso is slightly concave. Small incised dots form a diamond pattern over the right shoulder; parallel, short horizontal striations run down the left edge of the overgarment. Both the dove and the pomegranate which the lady carries seem to be cast in one piece with the figure. Note the life-size terracotta pomegranate probably used as a burial offering, No. 103 of this catalogue.

BIBLIOGRAPHY: Queens College Catalogue, p. 22, no. 143.
For the Fogg Museum piece, see G.M.A. Hanfmann, *Archaeology* 9 (1956), pp. 230-232 (ill.). For general remarks on Etruscan votive bronzes, see E.H. Richardson, *The Etruscans* (Chicago, 1965), pp. 132 ff. Compare also British Museum 613 and 612: Giglioli, *L'arte etrusca*, p. 40, pl. CCXXIII, 2 and 3.

127 Young Satyr

Possibly Fourth Century B.C.
Bronze with yellow-brown patina
Height: 10.9 cm (4⁵⁄₁₆ in.)

The youthful satyr seems to be dancing; his arms and
hands are posed as if perhaps a *patera* had been held in
the left hand and a pitcher in the right, but the hands
were clearly not intended to hold anything. The combination of pouring and dancing is most unusual.

The crown and back of the head is smooth, as if bald
or covered with a tight-fitting cap, with a fringe of locks
across the back of the head. The broken edges are dark
grey in color. Fingers, toes of left foot and tips of ears are
broken.

Mr. Pomerance remarks that there are two similar figures on the
Napoleon Cista in the Louvre, no. 1663. However, the style of the
face and modeling of the musculature are more Hellenistic or Roman
than Etruscan.

128 Winged Youth and Lion's Paw Support

Probably from Praeneste
Third Century B.C.
Bronze
Height: 12 cm (4¾ in.)

Feet of this sort supported tripods but more often *cistae*, bronze containers usually cylindrical and richly decorated with incised borders and figural scenes. *Cista* feet with winged figures in a one-knee bend are now in the Villa Giulia. They rest on a volute of the style of an Ionic capital; this youth, perhaps Eros, sits on what appears to be an altar which, in turn, surmounts the volute.

The lion's paw is pierced between the claws, and the square base is hollow. A small horizontal shelf projects at the back of the volute to provide additional support for the chest. A nail about .03 cm in diameter and .08 cm long extends on the back at right angles behind the top of the altar. Details of the feathering of the wings are incised.

Cf. *cista* feet with winged figures, Giglioli, *L'arte etrusca*, pls. CCXC, 1 and 6, and CCXCI, 2. A bronze *cista* with warriors and battle scenes is in the Metropolitan Museum of Art, acc.no. 22.84.1 a-b. The head of our "Eros" is similar in features and coiffure to those of the three figures of a *cista* handle also in the Metropolitan (09.221.11), dated to the fourth century.

129 Vase in Form of a Woman's Head

Late Third to Mid-Second Century B.C.
Bronze
Height: 11.0 cm (4⁵⁄₁₆ in.)

Probably used by Etruscan ladies for some sort of toilet articles, these head vases have been thought to represent Turan, goddess of love and beauty, or Lhassae, minor female divinities who may appear as assistants of Turan. A few may represent funerary deities. (GMAH)

The object probably had a lid, but there is no evidence that it was attached to the vase. The base appears to have been attached with a lead seam.

One such vase, in the Museum of Fine Arts, Boston (99.459), certainly represents a love goddess; two birds included in an elaborate headdress must be the doves associated with Aphrodite, the Greek goddess with whom Turan was identified. The head vase most similar to ours in size, coiffure and jewelry is British Museum no. 762, from Chiusi. For a thorough study of vases of this type, see S. Haynes and H. Menzel, "Etruskische Bronzekopfgefässe", *Jahrbuch des Römisch-Germanischen Zentralmuseums Mainz* 6 (1959), pp. 110-127, pls. 40-58, especially p. 117, Type III, no. 4, pl. 45, 1. D. von Bothmer suggests a fourth century date.

130 Beaked Jug

Fifth Century B.C.
Bronze
Height: 21 cm (8¼ in.)

Bronze was frequently used for vessels, particularly those which were buried with the dead. Jugs of this shape were part of a group of objects said to come from a tomb in Falerii (modern Civita Castellana), and now in the Metropolitan Museum. Variations occur in the shape of the terminals of the handles, which are sometimes in the form of heads of animals or satyrs or of leaves.

Cf. G.M.A. Richter. *Greek, Etruscan and Roman Bronzes* (New York, 1915), pp. 179-180, nos. 488-491 (Metropolitan Museum of Art acc.nos. 12.160.3, 12.160.2, 12.160.1, and 13.227.3). This type of oinochoe is called "Schnabelkanne" by Paul Jacobsthal who has written extensively on the vessel with Alexander Langsdorff in *Die Bronzeschnabelkannen, ein Beitrag zur Geschichte des vorrömischen Imports nördlich der Alpen* (Berlin-Wilmersdorf, 1929).

131 Ladle

Fifth Century B.C.
Bronze
Height, from base of bowl to highest point of bend of
   birds' necks: 29.2 cm (11⅕ in.)

The ladle handle terminates in two ducks' heads. An essential utensil for the preparation and serving of wine in banqueting convivial or funerary, this form is probably derived from the Phrygian ladles of the seventh century B.C., and probably came to the Etruscans and Romans through the Greeks. (DGM) Similar *simpula*, or ladles, are represented in wall paintings in both the Tomb of the Painted Vases and the Tomb of the Lionesses, Tarquinia, as part of the equipment accompanying the funeral celebration.

This ladle is covered with a brilliant turquoise-colored patina.

Several *simpula* can be seen in the Metropolitan Museum, with one and with two duck heads; 10.210.35 is a close parallel to the Pomerance ladle, differing in minor respects. It is said to come from Civita Castellana. The painted walls including ladles are illustrated in *Monumenti della pittura antica scoperti in Italia*, Sezione I, Tarquinii, Fasc. 1, and described by Pericle Ducati: for the Tomb of the Lionesses, p. 4, pls. I, III; for the Tomb of the Painted Vases, p. 12, pl. V,1;VI,1.

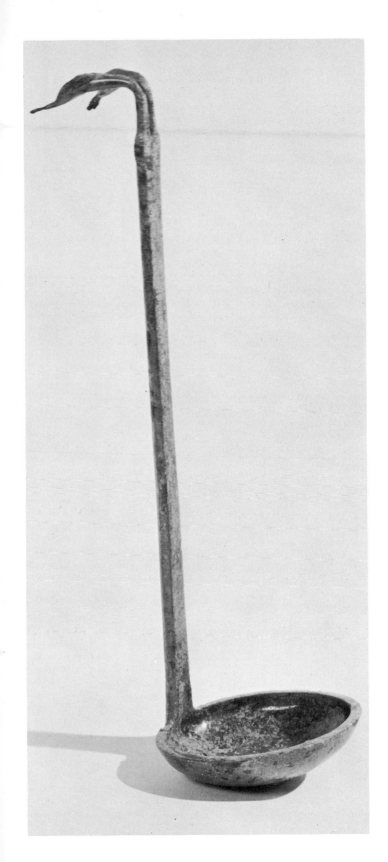

132   High-handled Cup

Fifth Century B.C.
Bronze, with brilliant patina predominantly turquoise,
    pale and dark blue-green.
Total height: 10.9 cm (4⁵⁄₁₆ in.) Height of cup: 7.2 cm
    (2¹¹⁄₁₆ in.)

Probably related to the *kyathos,* a one-handled drinking
cup or dipper in Attic pottery, this form, like the ladle
No. 131, has a long life well down into Roman Imperial
times. (DGM)

   A sandy earth incrustation remains inside. The slightly
concave base has a small central depression.

Several cups of this shape and material were found in a group of
vessels and other objects said to come from a tomb in Civita
Castellana, now in the Metropolitan Museum, among them acc.nos.
12.160.4 and 12.160.5. They vary in size and some have bands of
incised decoration below the shoulder or just below the handle
base. See Richter, *op. cit.* pp. 206 ff., nos. 570-574, ill. p. 179; no. 574
(acc.no. 13.277.4) is most similar. The shape also appears frequently in clay, as in Oxford 259; this is called the "Sant' Anatolia
shape" by Beazley in his *Etruscan Vase-Painting* (Oxford, 1947),
pp. 186, 263; pl. 38, 6.

133 Oinochoe

Late Fifth Century B.C.
Bronze, with pale blue-green patina
Total height: 16.1 cm (6⅝₆ in.)

The shape of the bronze jug with tall handle is long-lived, but this particular form is probably Late Etruscan or Roman Republican.

Cf. Richter, *op. cit.*, p. 194, no. 511, acc.no. 00.13.4. (GMAH) The slender proportions of the New York oinochoe are very like those of a gilded Etruscan jug in Boston (95.71). It is probably this more elongated shape that is represented in the hand of a nude boy who is approaching three large vessels on a "pediment" painting in the Tarquinian Tomb of Hunting and Fishing: *Monumenti della pittura antica scoperta in Italia*, Sez. I (1937), Fasc. II, Tav. C, and described by P. Romanelli, p. 14. Mrs. Richardson considers the more squat shape of the Pomerance bronze to be earlier than the Metropolitan oinochoe, or fifth century B.C.

134 Vessel

Bronze
Height: 14.9 cm (5⅞ in.)

The vase has a pale blue-green patina and is made of thin bronze. The bottom is scored in three concentric circles, the largest 5.8 cm in diameter. Two areas on opposite sides of the body appear to be repaired; one shows traces of an inlaid design.

No Etruscan parallels of this vessel shape are known to the author at this time; similar shapes do appear in the Chinese repertoire.

135 Antefix in Form of a Woman's Head

End of Sixth, Beginning of Fifth Century B.C.
Terracotta with traces of red and black paint
Height: 2 cm (10¼ in.)

Etruscan temples are believed to have been structures of
wood and sun-dried brick with vividly modeled and
painted terracotta entablatures. An antefix was used, as
in Greek architecture, to conceal tile joints at the eaves
of a roof; these were often decorated with palmettes or
with faces of silens, gorgons or, as here, with those of
human females. A hemicylindrical form extended horizontally to the rear from below the back of the head to
cover the meeting of the regular roofing tiles. The woman
wears a head cloth under the so-called *tutulus*, the typical
Etruscan hat, here decorated with a traditional tongue
pattern, red on the outer edges, black within the arches.
Her necklace includes three acorn-shaped *bullae*, beads
of pendant form found in Etruscan jewelry of the fourth
or third century B.C. It is possible that the antefix, ancient
in form, has been partially repainted.

A small hole (0.7 cm in diameter) pierces the crown of
the hat. A thin layer of slip appears to have covered the
coarse base clay. The hair is painted black, as are the eyes
and brows. The necklace is composed of black *bullae* on
red; the garment was probably red. The back is unpainted.

Professor Arvid Andrén remarks in a letter dated 19 February
1966 on two antefixes "found in 1939 . . . at a locality called Tre
Fontane, between Rome and Ostia . . ." which are very similar to the
Pomerance piece. These were recorded by Prof. P. E. Arias in *Le
Arti*, II (1939-1940), pp. 45 ff., fig. 5, and dated by him to the end of
the sixth or the beginning of the fifth century B.C. Two more antefixes,
similar in form to each other but with slight variations from the
present object, come from Tivoli (now in the Villa Giulia, Rome),
and from ancient Praeneste (now in Ny Carlsberg Glyptotek, Copenhagen). For the Tivoli piece and an excellent study of related objects,
see A. Andrén, *Architectural Terracottas from Etrusco-Italic Temples*
(Lund, Leipzig, 1940), particularly p. 370: Tivoli, Group I, 1, pl. 114,
no. 402; also A. Boethius, *et al.*, *Etruscan Culture, Land and People*
(New York, 1962), fig. 403. For the Praeneste antefix: Copenhagen
I.N. 426, see F. Poulsen, *Ny Carlsberg Glyptotek Katalog over Antike
Skulpturer* (Copenhagen, 1940), p. 39, no. 19; and *Billedtaver* (Copenhagen, 1907), pl. 2, no. 19.

136   Torso of a Woman

Early Fifth Century B.C.
Terracotta
Height: 13.5 cm (5⁵⁄₁₆ in.)

Reminiscent of Archaic Greek female statues, this small clay torso wears a mantle that clings to the back in a deep U-shape. It has been suggested that it is a sculptor's model.

The clay is bright red-orange, with shiny black and other inclusions. Traces of a buff-colored incrustation cover some areas of pink.

137   Olpe

Italo-Corinthian
End of Seventh Century B.C.
Yellow-buff terracotta with black glaze and white details
Height: 44.8 cm (17⁵⁄₈ in.)

The *olpe* was one of many pottery shapes devoted to the storing, pouring and consumption of wine. Our example is an Italic imitation of the Corinthian painting style popular throughout the Mediterranean world until the middle of the sixth century B.C. Exotic animals of Oriental inspiration graze and parade around the jug in a profusion of space-filling ornament. Stylized flowers or rosettes are depicted by an arrangement of dots, as on the neck and the decorative discs at the meeting of handle and mouth, and by "blots" with intersecting incised lines as on the body.

This *olpe* is reconstructed of several fragments.

BIBLIOGRAPHY: *Antike Kunstwerke, Auktion II,* 14 May 1960. Ars Antiqua A.G. Luzern, p. 47, no. 125, pl. 49.
In Munich, Museum antiker Kleinkunst, is an *olpe* of more slender proportions decorated with discs and animals rendered in much the same style, particularly the indication of shoulder muscles with a nearly circular incised line: P. Ducati, *Storia dell'arte etrusca* (Florence, 1927) Vol. I, p. 124, Vol. II pl. 33, no. 110 right. The Metropolitan Museum owns an Italo-Corinthian *olpe* (96.18.39) of slightly different shape, and dated 600-575 B.C.

138   Cinerary Jar

Late Seventh to Sixth Century B.C.
Terracotta
Height combined: 48.0 cm (18⅞ in.); height of head:
    23.5 cm (9¼ in.); height of jar: 30.0 cm (11¹³⁄₁₆ in.)

Jars with lids in the form of human heads were used by Etruscans for burial of ashes of the deceased particularly in the area around Chiusi, the ancient city of Clusium. The native strain of severe realism represented in this head reappears later in Hellenistic and Republican Roman portraits and terracottas. (DGM)

The head is repaired, with a band of restoration across the front neck edge and across the back of the neck up to the ears and hairline. The flat depressions of the eyes may indicate incrustation of another material. Holes for earrings are not unusual in these pieces, but rare in the upper ear; the left ear is not pierced, the right broken. The fabric of the head is red-brown terracotta and appears to have been polished before firing. The jar is either a coarser ware or unpolished, and ranges from red-orange to dark brown-black in color. An unusual feature is the opening of the nearly cylindrical arms into the main jar cavity; indeed, the profile is most similar to that of a "bucchero" *skyphos* in Florence, no. 2923 (Levi, article cited below, pl. 59, fig. 38).

D. Levi, "I Canopi di Chiusi," *La critica d'arte*, I (1935-1936), pp. 18-26, 82-89 and pls. 8-15, 56-59, cites several Chiusan examples; that most similar to this piece comes from Tomb no. 8 in Cancelli and is now in the Museo Archeologico di Firenze (pl. 56, fig. 28 and pl. 57, fig. 35). The head is more oblong and less flattened at the crown but shows two depressed areas for what must have been enormous eyes inlaid with another material. While jars with loop arms are common, rare examples of the stubby arms of the Pomerance jar can be found; in the Cancelli jar and in Levi, *op. cit.*, pl. 14, f. 17 left. I do not know, however, whether they are hollow as are the present arms.

139   Hydria with Two Handles

About 520 B.C.
Terracotta with black and white color
Height: 38.1 cm (15 in.)

A *hydria*, as its name implies, was used in the countries of the ancient Greek-speaking Mediterranean world for carrying water. Such a vessel usually had a third vertical handle from mouth to shoulder, midway between the other handles. The painting style of the vigorously **dancing men and women** and the more stately animals has been attributed to the Micali Painter by Beazley.

Vivid dancers and musicians are represented on the painted walls of several tombs in Tarquinia, notably the Tombs of the Leopards, of the Triclinium, and of the Lionesses. The participants are engaged, often with banqueters, in activities of life that would gladden the hearts of the dead.

Fine incised lines reinforce the folds of the drapery. There are some restorations. The front-folded head cloth appears also on No. 135, an antefix.

BIBLIOGRAPHY: *Ancient Art*, p. 66, no. 261, pls. 65, 96.
In letters dated 7 November 1953, and 30 December 1959, Beazley identifies the painter of the vase and refers to a neck amphora, Chiusi 577, illustrated in Giglioli, *L'arte etrusca*, pl. CXXX, 2. The Tomb of the Lionesses is illustrated in *Monumenti della pittura antica scoperta in Italia*, Sez. 1, Tarquinii, Fasc. 1 (1937), pl. A, I, III, pp. 4-5. The Tombs of the Leopards and the Triclinium are in Giglioli, *op. cit.*, pls. CCI and CCVII respectively.

140 Amphora with Animals

Sixth Century B.C.
Buff terracotta with red-brown
  and cream decoration
Height: 55 cm (21⅝ in.)

This Etruscan amphora is of the polychrome style which, as J. G. Szilagyi has shown, began about 620 B.C., and continued in use until the middle of the sixth century B.C.

The highly decorative frieze of figures includes a hippocamp, a winged lion, a grazing deer and a bird. The animals as well as the petal shaped decorations have been rendered with cream-colored slip over the main color, and structural and decorative details are accented with incised lines.

Cf. G.M.A. Hanfmann, *Bulletin of the Fogg Museum*, 3, 9 (1940), pp. 44-49; J. G. Szilagyi, "Italo-Corinthiaca," *Studi etruschi*, 26 (1958), pp. 273-284 quotes extensive literature on the subject. (GMAH) An oinochoe of similar fabric in the Metropolitan Museum (25.78.106) is decorated with animals, but has a tongue pattern around the shoulder and above the base. The Pomerance piece has rosettes around the shoulder. Similar animals—hippocamp and grazing deer—appear on Etruscan "bucchero" vessels in both New York and Boston.

142 Diadem

Said to be from Taranto
Third Century B.C.
Gold
Length: 33 cm (13 in.)

The ladies of Hellenistic times throughout the countries bordering on the Mediterranean were fascinated by fine jewelry, if we can judge from the variety of design and richness of material and workmanship that were lavished on articles of personal adornment. A diadem was worn around the head, sometimes over an up-swept coiffure, and could be simply or elaborately decorated.

On this diadem, fourteen rosettes are attached to a single band of gold that has scalloped and turned-up edges. Each flower is formed of two superimposed six-petal parts, the under larger than the upper, and the two secured in the center by a granulated sphere. The balls that emerge on short wires from between the petals of each flower are granulated on alternating rosettes.

BIBLIOGRAPHY: Queens College Catalogue, p. 24, no. 179; *Ancient Art*, p. 72, no. 283, pl. 102.
An earring in the Villa Giulia (no. 40881) contains a five-leaf rosette similar in construction to those of the diadem; however, it is in a much more elaborate setting; leaves, and granulated and wire borders and motifs. G. Becatti, in *Oreficerie antiche* (Rome, 1955), p. 182, no. 288, pl. LXXIV, dates the piece to the sixth century B.C., describing it as "Etrusco-Ionic" work. Other examples of Etruscan diadems generally more complicated in design and execution are noted by von Bothmer, *loc. cit.*
For an extensive study of technique and style of Hellenistic gold jewelry, see H. Hoffmann and P. Davidson, *Greek Gold, Jewelry from the Age of Alexander* (Brooklyn, 1965). Their no. 10 is a group of fifteen rosettes from the area of the Hellespont that are similar but more refined in design and workmanship; they may not have been intended as part of a diadem.

141 Oinochoe

Late Fourth Century B.C.
Buff terracotta
Height: 34.7 cm (13$\frac{11}{16}$ in.)

One of the several shapes of wine jug called "oinochoe," this particular vase is closest to the type VII of Beazley's classification that was widely used in Etruria and, indeed, was rare outside it and Latium. The shape appears with both red- and black-figure decoration, as well as in the simple black on buff scheme we see here.

Cf. Beazley, *Etruscan Vase-Painting* (Oxford, 1947), p. 268, no. 2, Group of Leyden 192 A (i), for the same shape, without lip, and dull black glazed without decoration.

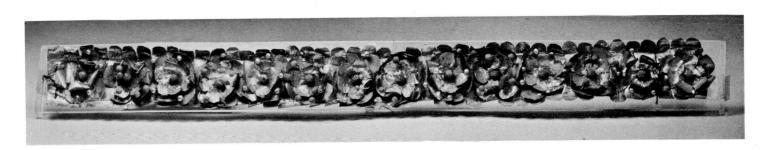

Kato Zakro

On September 13, 1963, Leon and Harriet Pomerance were to find themselves literally knee-deep in a treasury of Minoan Art of the sixteenth century B.C. The room was filled with one hundred vases in terracotta, rock crystal, alabaster, colored marble and obsidian used in the ritual services of a Cretan palace of the Middle Bronze age.

The Pomerances' interest in collecting ancient art had led them to wide reading in the field of archaeology. In the fall of 1960, Leon Pomerance had read a statement by Dr. Nikolas Platon, then director of the Museum of Herakleion, that there were still important sites unexcavated on the island of Crete.

The Pomerances were somewhat skeptical that sites of great significance might still be unknown in an area no larger than Long Island. Crete had been explored by European and American archaeologists since Arthur Evans' excavation of the Palace of Minos at Knossos at the turn of the century. Palaces had been found later at Mallia and Phaistos, and dozens of minor sites had been uncovered; by 1960 most archaeologists had little hope of finding yet another palace, particularly in eastern Crete, a rocky and forbidding landscape without the large arable valleys that were the base of the agricultural wealth of the other Minoan principalities.

With Dr. Platon's acceptance of modest financial assistance —on the understanding that the Pomerances could be present at the excavations—an expedition was formed in August 1962, to uncover the site of Kato Zakro. Additional help was obtained from the Greek Archaeological Society, and Dr. Platon brought to light the fourth great palace of Crete, one of the most sensational archaeological finds since World War II. Over 2,500 objects have since been uncovered, in bronze, ivory, terracotta, gold and stone, many of unique beauty and ingenuity. All of these objects, in accordance with Greek law, are now in the Museum of Herakleion in Crete.

The Pomerances feel well rewarded by the thrilling experience of having participated in this extraordinary find and the privilege of having been present with Dr. Platon at Kato Zakro. But, they report philosophically, as collectors they must confess to a feeling of some ambivalence in witnessing a Cretan worker lovingly unearth a 3,500-year-old vessel destined to remain where, in all justice, it belongs—with the Cretan people.

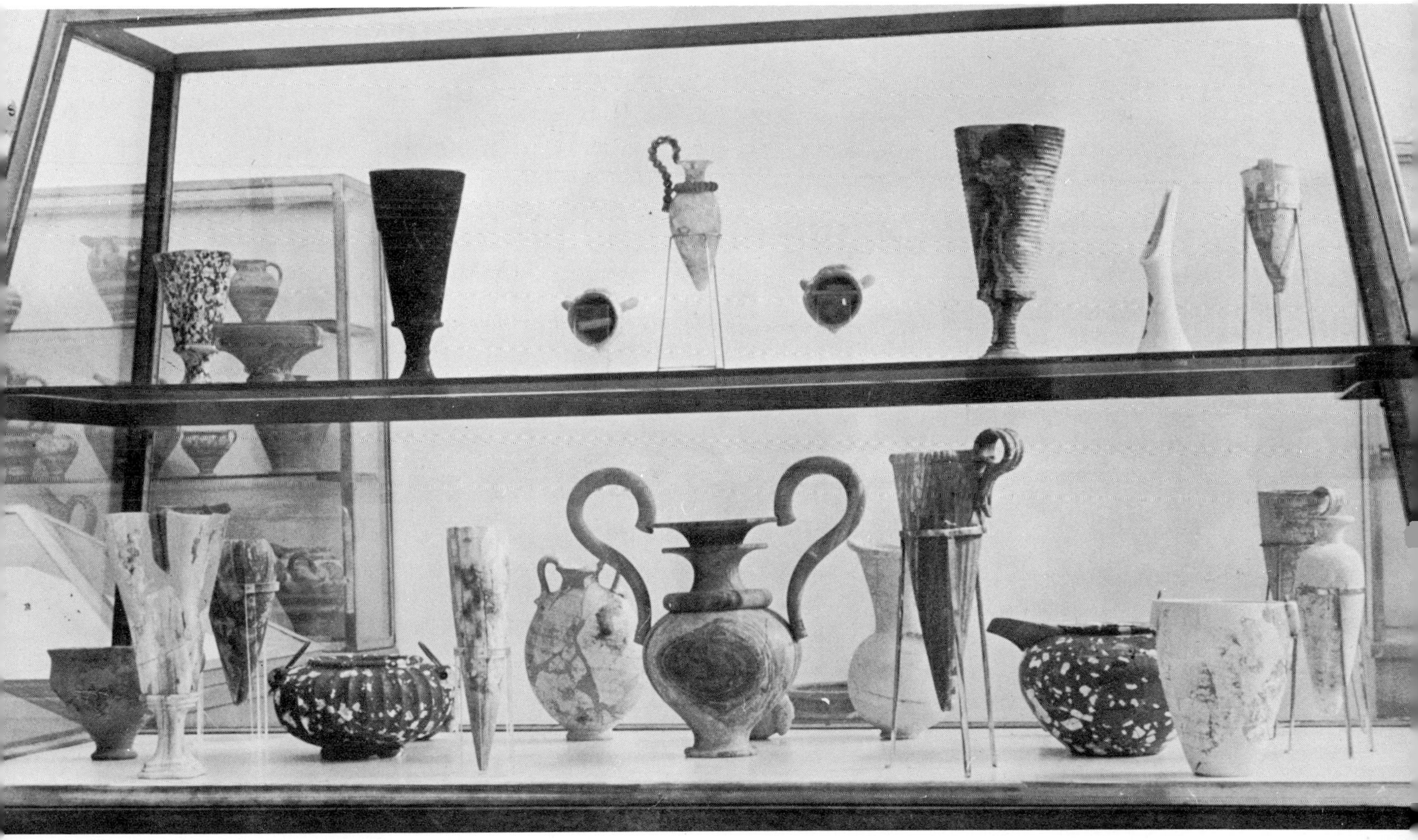

Case in the Zakro Room of the Herakleion Museum

Bibliography

The works listed here are intended as a guide
to more detailed bibliography.

Ancient Near East

Encyclopédie photographique de l'art. Le Musée du Louvre, I-II
 (Paris, 1936)

H. Frankfort, *The Art and Architecture of the Ancient Orient*(3rd
 revised impression, Baltimore, 1963)

——*Cylinder Seals* (London, 1939)

R. Ghirshman, *Art of Ancient Iran* (New York, 1964)

S. Lloyd, *The Art of the Ancient Near East* (New York, 1961)

A. Parrot, *Nineveh and Babylon* (London, 1961)

——*Sumer* (London, 1960)

E. Porada, *The Art of Ancient Iran* (New York, 1965)

Committee of Ancient Near Eastern Seals, *Corpus of Ancient Near
 Eastern Seals in North American Collections*, I. *The Collection of
 The Pierpont Morgan Library*, catalogued and edited by E. Porada
 with B. Buchanan (Washington, 1948)

J. B. Pritchard, ed., *Ancient Near Eastern Texts Relating to the Old
 Testament* (2nd edition, Princeton, 1955)

E. Strommenger, *Fünf Jahrtausende Mesopotamien* (Munich, 1960)
 English edition: *Five Thousand Years of the Art of Mesopotamia*
 (New York, 1964)

E. L. B. Terrace, *The Art of the Ancient Near East in Boston* (Boston, 1962)

Ancient Egypt

C. Aldred, *The Development of Ancient Egyptian Art* (London,
 1952)

J. D. Cooney, *Amarna Reliefs from Hermopolis in American Collections* (Brooklyn, 1965)

W. C. Hayes, *The Scepter of Egypt*, I-II (New York, 1959-60)

G. Posener *et al.*, *Dictionary of Egyptian Civilization* (New York,
 1962)

W. S. Smith, *Ancient Egypt* (Boston, 1960)

——*The Art and Architecture of Ancient Egypt* (Baltimore, 1954)

——*Interconnections in the Ancient Near East* (New Haven, 1965)

Ancient Greece

M. Bieber, *The Sculpture of the Hellenistic Age* (revised edition, New York, 1961)

J. Boardman, *Greek Art* (New York, 1964)

J. Charbonneaux, *Greek Bronzes* (New York, 1962)

R. M. Cook, *Greek Painted Pottery* (London, 1960)

F. Matz, *The Art of Crete and Early Greece* (New York, 1962)

Museum of Fine Arts, Boston, *Greek, Etruscan and Roman Art, The Classical Collections of the Museum of Fine Arts* (Boston, 1963)

J. V. Noble, *The Techniques of Painted Attic Pottery* (New York, 1965)

G. M. A. Richter, *A Handbook of Greek Art* (London, 1959)

_____*The Sculpture and Sculptors of the Greeks* (3rd edition, New Haven, 1950)

M. Robertson, *Greek Painting* (Geneva, 1959)

E. T. Vermeule, *Greece in the Bronze Age* (Chicago, 1964)

T. B. L. Webster, *Greek Terracottas* (London, 1950)

Etruria

A. Boethius *et al.*, *Etruscan Culture, Land and People* (New York, 1962)

G. Q. Giglioli, *L'arte etrusca* (Milan, 1935)

M. Pallottino, *Etruscan Painting* (Geneva, 1952)

_____*The Etruscans* (Aylesbury, 1955)

M. Pallottino, W. Dräyer and M. Hürlimann, *Art of the Etruscans* (London and Zurich, 1955)

E. Richardson, *The Etruscans, Their Art and Civilization* (Chicago and London, 1964).